PPROBLEM
SSSOLVING

Thomas C. DeFranco, Ph.D.
University of Connecticut

Charles I. Vinsonhaler, Ph.D.
University of Connecticut

THOMSON
CUSTOM PUBLISHING

Editor: Julie Howell
Production Manager: Staci Powers
Production Coordinator: Mary Snelling
Marketing Coordinator: Sara L. Hinckley

Printed in the United States of America

Thomson Learning Custom Publishing
5191 Natorp Blvd.
Mason, Ohio 45040
USA

For information about our products, contact us:
1-800-355-9983
http://www.custom.thomsonlearning.com

International Headquarters
Thomson Learning
International Division
290 Harbor Drive, 2nd Floor
Stamford, CT 06902-7477
USA

UK/Europe/Middle East/South Africa
Thomson Learning
Berkshire House
168-173 High Holborn
London WCIV 7AA

Asia
Thomson Learning
60 Albert Street, #15-01
Albert Complex
Singapore 189969

Canada
Nelson Thomson Learning
1120 Birchmount Road
Toronto, Ontario MIK 5G4
Canada
United Kingdom

Visit us at www.e-riginality.com and learn more about this book and other titles published by Thomson Learning Custom Publishing

ISBN 0-7593-1013-0

The Adaptable Courseware Program consists of products and additions to existing Custom Publishing products that are produced from camera-ready copy. Peer review, class testing, and accuracy are primarily the responsibility of the author(s).

PPROBLEM
SSSOLVING

Thomas C. DeFranco, Ph.D.
University of Connecticut

Charles I. Vinsonhaler, Ph.D.
University of Connecticut

TABLE OF CONTENTS

Chapter 1

THE PROBLEM-SOLVING ENTERPRISE

OK, Houston we've had a problem here.

---John L. Swigert Jr.
CM Pilot, Apollo 13

On April 13, 1970, the world watched and collectively held its breath after John L. Swigert Jr., command module pilot of Apollo 13, spoke those seven words. Over the

next four days NASA scientists worked feverishly to solve a variety of problems plaguing the astronauts and the ship. Facing tremendous odds, NASA personnel worked in teams, rewrote procedures, modeled and tested routines and apparatus, and brought the astronauts safely back to earth. It was a triumph for humankind and an example of problem solving at its best!

We all have problems-and lots of them. Most are not as complex and life threatening as those encountered by the astronauts, but nevertheless they occupy a good deal of our time and energy. The good news is we can learn to be better problem solvers. The catch is that it doesn't happen overnight. As the Buddhists say, you can't be shown enlightenment; you can only be shown the path. To start you down the path, this book will hit you in the head, like Raffiki hit Simba in The Lion King. But instead of a stick, we wield a collection of challenging and engaging problems. You will study a variety of techniques that can power you down the path to enlightened problem solving. The joy is in the journey, so let's get started.

What is a Problem?

Problems come in many forms and degrees of difficulty. Defining the term "problem" is a problem because it is a relative term - what may be a difficult problem for one individual may be an easy exercise for another. The following definition, taken from the *Oxford English Dictionary*, best captures how the term is used in this book: "A doubtful or difficult question; a matter of inquiry, discussion, or thought; a question that exercises the mind."

The problems in this book come from a broad spectrum of disciplines. While many of the problems are mathematical in nature, the emphasis is on creative thinking rather than advanced mathematical techniques - little is required in the way of background.

Why Learn to Solve Problems?

We believe, and will repeat frequently, that anyone can learn to be a better problem solver. The benefits of such an improvement should be obvious, but let's examine a few.

- Problem-solving skills can be used in any classroom, on problems ranging from writing an essay on Romeo and Juliet, to conducting a laboratory exercise in Physics. For example, students who use problem-solving skills effectively have an easier time deciding how much time and energy to put into a classroom assignment or in studying for an exam.

- The problem-solving skills you learn in a mathematics class can be adapted easily to situations in the real world. For example, the effective use of problem-solving skills can help you in your everyday life involving interpersonal problems (see Chapter 8), improved time management, a sharper focus on what is important to you, a keener interest in lifelong learning, and an increased confidence in yourself to complete a task. These are all benefits that students have found following on the heels of an improved capacity to solve problems.

In the final analysis, the better we are at solving problems, the more satisfaction and happiness we will derive from life.

Types of Problems.

Some problems are clearly formulated and contain all the information you need to solve them. Such problems, like those found in standard textbooks, might be called routine problems. Other problems, called non-routine, demand that the investigator gather information, make assumptions, estimate quantities, and decide what the final answer should look like. It is helpful to develop your ability to assess problems in this regard. For each of the following problems, decide whether you think it is a routine or non-routine problem. In the latter case, list the information, assumptions, and estimates that may be needed, along with the form of the final answer.

Changing 50 Cents

In how many ways can you change one-half dollar? (Note: The way of changing is determined if it is known how many coins of each kind-quarters, dimes, nickels, pennies are used.)

A Heap of Beans

There are 16 beans in a pile. Two people playing against each other take turns removing either 1, 2, or 3 beans from the pile on each turn. The person who removes the last bean(s) wins the game. Describe a winning strategy for this game.

Body Cells

How many cells might be found in an averaged-sized adult human body? What is a reasonable upper estimate? A reasonable lower estimate? (Hint: What size magnification on a microscope would you need to see a cell?)

Some Early Examples of Problems

Some of the earliest examples of mathematics problems can be found in the writings of the ancient Egyptians, Chinese, and Greeks. The Ahmes Papyrus, (circa 1650 B.C.) consists of a collection of problems copied from an earlier Egyptian manuscript, while the following problem comes from a Chinese document dating back to about 1000 B.C.

Of two water weeds, the one grows 3 feet and the other 1 foot on the first day. The growth of the first becomes everyday half of that of the preceding day while the other grows twice as much as on the day before. In how many days will the two grow to equal heights? (Stanic and Kilpatrick [31, p. 2]).

Another example can be found in the writings of the ancient Greeks:

I am a brazen lion; my spouts are my two eyes, my mouth and the flat of my right foot. My right eye fills a jar in two days, my left eye in three, and my foot in four. My mouth is capable of filling it in six hours; tell me how long all four together will take to fill it (Stanic and Kilpatrick [31, p. 3]).

With a few word changes, these problems sound remarkably similar to problems you may have encountered in your own mathematics classes.

Although problems have been around for a long time, learning to solve them still remains difficult. Compounding the difficulty is the fact that most of us are never taught how to systematically approach and attack problems, let alone how to develop these skills through practice. Our book is intended to remedy this deficiency. We won't place a strong emphasis on algebra and higher mathematics and we won't be using a lot of technical jargon. But as background, we do want you to know what researchers have found out about expert problem solvers.

Problem-solving experts possess certain key attributes including:

- **Knowledge** - Solving a problem requires that an individual possesses the requisite knowledge to solve the problem. Sometimes this knowledge is readily apparent or available, while other times you may have to consult a friend or find the information in the library. Once again, for the problems in this book, little is required in the way of formal mathematical knowledge. We will, however, stress the importance of gathering information, in particular by asking questions.

- **Problem-Solving Strategies** - Researchers found that expert problem solvers depend on and frequently use a variety of problem-solving strategies when solving problems. These strategies, commonly referred to as *heuristics*, were made popular by G. Polya [24] in his book, *How To Solve It*. "Heuristic strategies are rules of thumb for successful problem solving, general suggestions that help an individual to understand a problem better or to make progress toward its solution" (Schoenfeld [27, p. 23]). A list of some of the more commonly used strategies or heuristics include: a) making a table or chart to help organize information, b) examining individual cases and looking for patterns in a problem, c) recalling a similar problem and its solution, d) working backward, and e) trial and error, just to name a few. These and many more strategies will be examined in detail later on in the book, in a format designed for ease of recall.

- **Metacognitive Skills** - The ability to monitor and reflect on the progress one makes while solving a problem is an essential component of successful problem solving. The phenomenon of creating an "inner voice and arguing with oneself" directs and oversees the entire problem-solving process and is metacognitive (i.e., helps you to think about thinking) in nature. This reflective process is the heart of the problem-solving enterprise.

- **Positive Beliefs About Problem Solving**- Beliefs concerning perseverance, confidence, motivation, interest, etc. with respect to mathematics contribute significantly to an individual's effort and performance on a problem. A particular belief system or view of mathematics may guide or influence an individual to select, change, abandon, pursue, or monitor strategies while solving a problem. Acquiring a set of positive beliefs about problem solving may motivate you to begin and persevere on difficult problems.

- **Practice** - There is an old story of a young musician, standing on a street corner in New York, who appeared lost and asked a pedestrian the following question: "Excuse me, but how do you get to Carnegie Hall"? The pedestrian replied, "Practice, practice, practice". This advice has never been truer than in solving problems. According to Polya [24, pp. 4-5],

  > Solving problems is a practical skill like, let us say, swimming. We acquire any practical skill by imitation and practice.... Trying to solve problems, you have to observe and to imitate what other people do when solving problems and, finally, you learn to do problems by doing them.

Together these components comprise the Problem-Solving Enterprise and they greatly influence the way one makes progress on a problem and ultimately how successful one is in solving it.

In the chapters that follow, we will deliver these components in small, easy to carry packages, with lots of opportunity for hands-on practice. For now, read through some of the problems in the following list of Suggested Exercises. They can be found, in alphabetical order, in Chapter 11. As you read a problem, record your response to it in terms of the attributes discussed above. For example, some questions you may want to address include:

- Do you have enough knowledge to solve the problem?

- If you have enough knowledge to solve the problem what approach or strategies would you employ to begin the problem?

- If you do not have enough knowledge to solve the problem where or how would you gather the needed information?

- Do you believe you can solve the problem? Why or why not?

- Reflect on your thoughts about the problem. Were they helpful or not?

- Practice by recording problems that you encounter over the next day or two in all aspects of your life.

Suggested Projects: *Different Angle, Inequality, Laser Treatment, Maple Tree, Largest Lake, Pearls, Shoreline*

Chapter 2

PPROBLEM SSSOLVING - FIVE EASY PIECES

In mathematics, know-how is much more important than mere possession

of information...What is know-how in mathematics? The ability to solve

problems –not merely routine problems but problems requiring some

degree of independence, judgment, originality, creativity.

---G. Polya

Nobody can be a good reasoner unless by constant practice he has

realized the importance of getting hold of the big ideas and hanging onto

them like grim death.

---Alfred North Whitehead

We have seen what skills experts find valuable in solving problems. But most of

us are not experts. How does a non-expert move further down the problem-solving path?

Many books have been written on problem solving—our approach differs in several

important ways from all others. First, we don't assume any mathematical expertise on the

part of the reader. In fact, a majority of the students we have taught from this book

readily admit that they come into the class "hating" mathematics. This is unfortunate, but

it provides the instructor with an excellent opportunity to show that mathematics is more than learning rules and how to apply them. Second, we include a liberal dose of non-mathematical problems. The kind of creative, critical thinking that epitomizes mathematics at its best can be applied to solving problems in any walk of life.

In this book you will study fundamental strategies and techniques that will enable to you to attack and solve problems which at first look impossible, problems from a broad spectrum of disciplines - mathematics, politics, psychology. While many of the examples are mathematical in nature, little is required in the way of background. Nonetheless, you will be analyzing and solving problems that have befuddled even Ph.D. mathematicians. What you will learn is powerful and exciting.

How do we learn to think critically and creatively? Experience has shown us that learners find it helpful to have a handful of rubrics or guideposts to help them begin, continue, and complete the problem solving process. To fulfill this need we group the methods we apply to problem solving into five basic strategies. To help fix these strategies in your mind, we label them with a **P** or an **S**, the leading letters of **P**Problem **SSS**olving. The strategies are:

Be Proactive
See it
Simplify it
Stir it up
Pause and Reflect

We hasten to emphasize that these are not rules or specific steps that you take to solve a problem. They are not intended to be followed in order. Rather they are to serve as pointers that give you direction down the path. The PSSSP strategies intertwine, diverge and recombine in ways that are unique to the individual traveler. Each problem solver needs to find his own way, guided by these strategies. Only experience can teach which directions are the most effective. We'll begin with a brief overview of each of the five strategies, and then illustrate their efficacy with an example.

BE PROACTIVE. To Be Proactive is to favor action. Be Positive. Plunge in. This strategy, which we will employ again and again in a variety of settings, has a simple primary message when you are confronted with a problem to solve: Get into it! The most fundamental idea in solving a problem is that you must commit to engage it. Levine [18] uses the term "intimate engagement" for the act of  resolving to give a problem your best shot. Sound simple? Most of us, when confronted with a problem, think about it for a few minutes and if the answer doesn't come immediately, we give up. We don't take the time to become meaningfully involved. Pause and reflect for a few moments on the last 24 hours in your life. Can you come up with an example of a problem you didn't solve because you walked away from it? On the other hand, think about a significant problem that you did solve recently. Chances are the solution began with a serious commitment on your part to finding an answer.

Why are we so reluctant to Be Proactive? In the face of a difficult problem, inertia is hard to overcome. In many problem situations, it's easier to do nothing, to procrastinate. A subtler barrier is erected by our egos. We don't have confidence in our ability to solve problems and we don't want to "look bad" by failing. One of our goals in this book is to help you realize that you are a good problem solver; to astound and excite you by bringing out the mental skills you don't realize you have. You can begin a marvelous cycle of confidence and competence reinforcing each other.

Stephen Covey [8], in *The Seven Habits of Highly Successful People*, lists *Be Proactive* as the first habit on his list. The principle is fundamental to your success as a learner in your journey through this book. Commit yourself right now to tackle the exercises, so that you can learn to deal with the frustration, and experience the joy of insight and accomplishment that characterize problem solving. Ask questions fearlessly, challenge your intellect on a regular basis, and take responsibility for keeping your mind and body in tune. These and other proactive streams will be examined in more detail in the next chapter and throughout the book. They can feed the flow of your problem solving until it becomes a powerful river of change—change in your day-to-day activities, change in your self-esteem, even change in your IQ!

SEE IT. Visual images, that is, things to see, help our minds assimilate and manipulate an overload of information. We've all experienced the limits of active memory - if I ask you to add the numbers 4352 and 1278 in your head, you can probably do it. But

what if I ask you to multiply them? Your active memory can handle only so much information at one time, so sketches, charts, and lists, pictures and other images you can put on paper, are powerful problem-solving aids. Models that you construct and manipulate with your hands are another way to See through a problem. If, as in the *Heap of Beans* example worked below, a problem asks about a game involving beans, go get a handful of beans that you can move around to gain insight. If you don't have access to beans, you can substitute, by tearing up some small pieces of paper, for example. A less tangible, but highly effective and underutilized way of seeing is the technique of using mental images, visualization. Most peak performing athletes will describe how they visualize a successful performance before they ever make a single move in competition. You can use the same methods on everyday problems.

SIMPLIFY IT. Time after time, a complicated problem becomes easy if you look at a simple version of it or break it into smaller pieces. Generally, when mathematicians are asked to solve problems, they begin by examining individual cases of the problem in order to get a "feel" for the problem and gain some insight in how to approach and solve the problem. For example, if a problem asks about 20 people, begin the problem with the case of 1 person, 2 people, 3 people, etc. You can record your results and insights in the simpler

cases (See it), look for patterns, and often extend to the general solution much more rapidly than if you try to chew and digest the whole problem as one mouthful. The power of this strategy in helping you to solve a problem cannot be overemphasized. Research verifies the effectiveness of starting small. Another simplification technique is to take a problem that is stated in general terms and make it more specific, more concrete. Look at a particular example. The problem becomes easier and in solving the easier version you may well see how your methods can be adapted to solving the original. We discuss the many ways to simplify problems in Chapter 5.

STIR IT UP. Sometimes the best technique for solving a problem is

to just try something. Be Proactive and plunge in. Make a guess and see if it works. If not, try a different guess. Create and manipulate a model. Think laterally - is there another problem you have solved that looks like this one? Can the problem be approached from a different angle? Try standing on your head. Brainstorm with others if you can. Even talking about a problem to a friend can help you clarify it in your own mind. Some psychologists go so far as to advocate "Talk first, then think." The idea is that by verbalizing questions and ideas you can trigger creativity.

PAUSE AND REFLECT. Research has shown that two important components in learning are first, to take an active role in the learning process (Be Proactive) and second, to Reflect systematically on what you have learned. Monitoring one's progress throughout the problem-solving process is a key component for problem-solving success. There is never an

inappropriate time in the problem-solving process to **Pause and Reflect** to help monitor your work. Some general questions to keep in mind when monitoring your work include:

- What type of answer should I expect?

- What is the unknown? What are the data of the problem?

- What is the relevant information of the problem?

- Can I recall a similar problem to the one I'm solving?

- What approach or strategy can I use on the problem? Is the plan or approach appropriate?

- Have I checked my plan or strategy prior to solving the problem? While in the midst of solving the problem?

- Have I checked my calculations while solving the problem?

- Does my answer check out?

- Can I derive the result differently?

- How can what I've learned be used at a later date?

Let's illustrate the five **PSSSP** strategies with an example from the last chapter.

A Heap of Beans.

> You and a friend are playing a game with a pile of 16 beans. You alternate turns and on each turn you must remove 1,2 or 3 beans from the heap. The player to remove the last bean(s) from the pile wins. Should you go first or second? Describe a winning strategy.

P: This is an easy game to play, but can be annoyingly resistant to analysis unless you commit to a determined and systematic approach. You need to be Proactive.

S: How do we See the problem more clearly? The most obvious way is to collect 16 beans, to obtain a model for the problem. Of course, you don't have to use beans—you can use pennies, pebbles or even torn-up pieces of paper.

S: Then you can Stir it up by playing the game. This helps you to engage the problem more intimately, to become familiar with it. Perhaps this was enough. By playing the game repeatedly you arrived at a solution.

P: If so, you can Pause and Reflect - check your answer by challenging your instructor to a game.

S: If you can't beat the instructor, maybe you can employ the one strategy we haven't mentioned yet: maybe you can Simplify it. What if there is only one bean in the pile. Clearly you want it to be your move. The same is true of a two-bean or three-bean heap. What if the heap has four beans? Probably you discovered in your Stirring that now the player who goes second wins. What about with five beans?

S: We can See more clearly the information we have discovered if we organize it in a chart (see chart on next page). Complete the chart, by filling in the rows for 6,7,8 and so on up to 16 beans.

Number of Beans	Winning Player	Strategy
1	1st Player	Take 1
2	1st Player	Take 2
3	1st Player	Take 3
4	2nd Player	Take Rest of Pile
5	1st Player	Take 1—Leave 4
6		
7		
8		
9		
10		
11		
12		
13		
14		
15		
16		

Now is a good time to **Pause and Reflect**.

- Do you know how to win the game?

- What strategies were the most helpful in solving the problem?

- What have you learned about games like this? For example,

  - What if the number of beans in the heap is changed?

  - What if the number of beans you can remove is changed?

  - What if there is more than one heap?

  - What generalizations can you derive about the *Heap of Beans* problem?

Formulate your own bean game. See if you can determine a winning strategy.

Here are some additional problems on which to test your **PProblem SSSolving** skills.

Suggested Projects: *Bouncing Bishop, Commuter, Four Bean Heaps, Grilled Cheese, Milk and Coffee, Planetary Voyage, Polyominoes, Seven Elevators, Stacking Rulers, Two Bean Heaps.*

Chapter 3

BE PROACTIVE

Success ... seems to be connected to action. Successful people keep moving. They make mistakes, but they don't quit.

--- Conrad Hilton

I was sufficiently interested to pursue the subject.

--- Alexander Fleming

Some philosophers have imagined that to start an inquiry it was only necessary to utter a question or set it down on paper, and have even recommended us to begin our studies with questioning everything! But the mere putting of a proposition into the interrogative form does not stimulate the mind to any struggle after belief. There must be a real and living doubt, and without this all discussion is idle.

--- C.S. Peirce

Make a Commitment. In the first chapter we emphasized the importance of "getting into" a problem, of making a serious commitment to the task of finding a solution. The point bears repeating. Unwillingness to engage a problem, for whatever reason, is probably the most common cause of failure. As C.S. Peirce

notes, the mere posing of a problem does not motivate you to think critically about it. On the other hand, meaningful confrontation may do so. As you read through these notes, you will be given repeated opportunities to lock problems in combat. Resolve again to do that. Any engagement exposes us to pain - the pain of a broken heart in a love affair, the pain of loss in athletic competition, the pain of failure in a business adventure. But only through exposing ourselves to this experience do we obtain the corresponding joys of success. Even if you never have before, you can experience the joy of solving mathematical problems. The confidence and skill you acquire can spread that joy to other areas of your life. Make a commitment, it's worth it.

Here's an example from Chapter 1 of a problem that needs little more than a firm commitment to solve it.

Changing 50 cents.

> In how many ways can you change one-half dollar? (Note: The way of changing is determined if it is known how many coins of each kind- quarters, dimes, nickels, pennies are used.)

A research study (DeFranco, [11]) on problem solving asked 16 Ph.D. mathematicians to solve this simple problem. Although there are a number of ways to solve it, ranging from a brute force method of enumerating all the cases to much more sophisticated mathematical counting techniques, those who were successful recognized the best approach was to count a few cases and look for a pattern—they plunged in and simply counted all the cases. Think about these mathematicians the next time you encounter a problem. An honest commitment to a problem will get you started on the problem and help you learn to overcome the anxiety and frustration caused by solving problems.

Get a Grip—Understanding the Problem. The importance of establishing a firm grasp on a problem as a first step in the solution can't be overemphasized. How can we possibly solve a problem we don't understand? And yet, time after time we encounter folks trying to get somewhere without knowing present location or intended destination. If someone stopped to ask you directions and couldn't tell you where he wanted to go, what would be your response? Here's a dialogue well known to teachers.

Student: I can't solve this problem.

Teacher: What does the problem ask?

Student: Something about power.

Teacher: Read it to me.

Student: How much power is required to lift a weight of 300 pounds

1 foot in height in one second?

Teacher: What is power?

Student: I don't know.

To repeat, you can't solve a problem if you don't understand it. Here are some questions you can ask to help you get a grip on a problem and understand it.

- Do I know what all the words mean?

- What is the relevant information in the problem?

- Will drawing a figure or introducing appropriate notation help?

- Are there any problems I have encountered before that are similar to this one?

- What is the unknown or goal of the problem?

- What should the solution look like?

- What conditions or restrictions do I need to take into account?

- How do these conditions relate to the goal of the problem?

- Are there any apparent approaches to try?

Each time you are confronted with a problem, challenge your understanding with questions like these. Then, when you feel you have a firm grip, test yourself by trying to explain the problem to someone else. Not only will you clarify the task at hand, you may enlist extra hands to help with the work. Get a grip on it.

Ask Questions. One of the most effective ways to solve a problem is to ask someone who knows the answer. For any subject, there is always someone who knows more than you do. Did you ever try to read a computer manual? It's a lot easier to ask questions of someone who knows what keys to press than to dig answers out of a manual. A university, in particular, is a vast network of expertise and information. Ask questions.

There are other effective ways to get information, of course. The good old-fashioned library not only has books, it has people who are very effective in seeking out information. Ask questions. A good new-fashioned source of information is the Internet. If you haven't already, learn how to use a web browser, and hit the information highway. It's done electronically, but the principle is the same. Ask questions.

Take care of your tools. The old saying goes, "Take care of your tools and they'll take

care of you." This is especially true when it comes to your problem-solving tools. Studies indicate that through practice we can improve our thinking, raise our intellectual capacity. But as another old saying goes, "If you want to fly, that cocoon has to go." Here are some practices that will help you spread those mental butterfly wings. They have been shown by research to be effective in improving analytical thinking.

- **Right state of body and mind.** If you are relaxed, rested and settled in a quiet place ready to work, your chances of solving a problem are increased.

- **Music.** Listening to music with 55-65 beats per minute can lead to more effective intellectual performance. Mozart is a recommended composer, but suitable modern music is available also (see Appendix).

- **Exercise and diet.** A healthy, properly nourished body is the best support for an effective mind.

- **Visualization**. Many authors, dating back to Norman Vincent Peale, have recommended the power of positive thinking. Try to run an internal video of "Putting on a Problem-Solving Hat," or some other positive visual image, each time you begin work on a problem. Visualization will be examined further in Chapter 4.

- **Triggers**. If you set up a regular routine to prepare for a session of hard thinking, the very act of performing that routine can sharpen your mental tools. Maybe it's a steaming cup of tea on your desk, or your favorite table at the library that will trigger your problem-solving mechanism.

- **Stimulation**. Like a muscle, the brain performs better if it has been exercised regularly.

A Gamesworth

Let's examine that last item (i.e., Stimulation) more closely. How much time do we spend in critical thought each day? For most of us, I suspect the answer is: not very much. If everyone devoted an hour a day to hard thinking - about social and environmental problems, relationships, helping the disadvantaged - the world would change dramatically. The prominent physicist M.L. Goldberger said, "There are some problems you cannot solve in a million years unless you think about them for 5 minutes." And the great Isaac Newton, when asked how he solved so many problems replied, "By always thinking about them." Carl Jung went even further: "The serious problems in life are never fully solved. If ever they should appear to be so it is a sure sign that something has been lost. The meaning and purpose of a problem seem to lie not in its solution but in our working at it incessantly. This alone preserves us from stultification and petrefaction."

As a measure of how much stimulation our brain needs to increase its performance level, Platt [21] defined a *gamesworth* as the amount of reasoning we can do at one sitting. A gamesworth is playing a game of chess, or solving a difficult crossword puzzle, or writing a three page essay - roughly an hour's time. Not so very long, since hard thinking is hard work. Even the great geniuses of history at their peaks did not 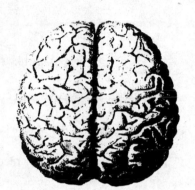 produce more than a gamesworth a day: Shakespeare completed 2 plays a year, Mozart an opus every two weeks, and Euler a thousand pages of mathematics a year. Somerset Maugham, the English author and playwrite, said, "If you can't become rich and famous by writing until noon, you can't do it by writing all day either."

To improve your problem-solving skills, immerse yourself in a gamesworth assignment regularly. Your task is to think deeply about one or more problems for around an hour. To help you benefit from this stimulation, keep a record of key points in your thought process. For example, you can record:

- Your interpretation of the problem

- Possible uses of PSSSP

- Specific ideas that seem promising

- Your feelings

Periodically writing down what you are trying to do helps develop an internal monitor that is a critical component of effective problem solving. Most of us tend to head off down attractive side roads instead of keeping on the highway that leads to a goal. Good problem solvers constantly remind themselves of where they're going. Pause regularly to write, "Where am I?" as you move through the process of looking for answers. Then make sure you can answer your own question.

Recording ideas has several benefits. It prolongs the good feeling that comes with an insight. Reward yourself by writing a big YES! when an idea comes. Recording also helps to check if the idea was a useful one (clear writing = clear thinking). Perhaps most critical is the fact that by recording your wrong ideas, you will keep yourself from going down the same back road over and over again. It's important to fail - no successful person is without some significant failures in her history. The key is to learn from your mistakes - don't repeat them. A psychologist, Roy John, did studies of people trying to perform mechanical tasks. He found that his subjects would punch the exact same wrong sequence of buttons up to twenty times before eliminating it. You can avoid such pitfalls by learning to jot down failures.

Believe it or not, it's useful to record feelings. If you feel good about taking a step toward a solution, treat yourself by describing your good feeling in writing, along with the big YES! You earned it. On the other hand, if you get stuck, say so. Write a big I'M STUCK! in the middle of the page. It will help you learn that it's ok to be stuck, and will trigger you to Pause and Reflect, to put down your hammer, go to your problem-solving tool chest and pull out another implement that may be more appropriate for the job.

Enjoy your gamesworths, the luxury of thinking hard about a problem without the pressure of having to "get an answer." Not all problems have answers, but you can always benefit from the stimulation, the mental exercise of looking for them. See if a regular gamesworth doesn't bring you satisfaction, increased confidence and a more relaxed attitude about tackling problems.

Suggested Stretches: *1 - 7*

Suggested Projects: *Body Cells, Percolation, Pick's Theorem, Shoreline, Six Digits, Square Roots, Symmetry*

Chapter 4

SEE IT

Thus the task is not so much to see what no one yet has seen, but to think what nobody yet has thought about that which everybody sees.

---Schopenhauer

The real voyage of discovery consists not in seeking new landscapes but in having new eyes.

---Marcel Proust

The word "see" has rich layers of meaning, beyond mere sensing with the eyes. Look up the word in a dictionary - the definition is one of the longest in the book. One of the ways to improve your problem solving is to develop your own unique talents for "seeing." In this chapter we discuss some standard techniques that help you see information more clearly by organizing it, visualizing it, contextualizing it, or creating a model to represent it. Typically this involves making a table, a chart, a figure, a graph, or using physical objects.

Tables and Charts

Many problems require that you keep track of information. Using a table or a chart is often helpful and may reveal a pattern that suggests ways to solve the problem completely. See how long it takes you to find the pattern in the next example.

The Green's Party

The Greens were having a party and were unsure how many guests they had invited. The night of the party, the first time the doorbell rang 1 guest entered the house. On the second ring, 3 guests entered. On the third ring, 5 guests entered. As it turned out, on each successive ring the entering group was 2 guests larger than the previous group. How many guests entered on the 15th ring and how many guests in total were in the house after the 15th ring?

A table can help keep track of the number of guests that enter the house and the total number of guests in the house. Information with respect to the first six rings has been entered in the table below. You should be able to complete the table to solve the problem.

Ring Number	Size of Entering Group	Total Number of Guests
1	1	1
2	3	4
3	5	9
4	7	16
5	9	25
6	11	36
...	...	...

Did the numbers in the table suggest a pattern that helped you complete the table and answer the question? If so, reflect on the pattern you discovered. Use your pattern to answer the following questions: How many guests entered on the 50th ring? How many total guests were in the house after the 50th ring?

Prom Problem

After the senior prom, six friends went to their favorite restaurant, where they shared a booth. The group consisted of the senior class president, the valedictorian, the head cheerleader, a player on the school volleyball team, a player on the school basketball team, and the school principal's only child. Their names were Betty, Frank, Gina, Joe, Ron, and Sally, not necessarily in that order. Each of the six was in love with one of the others of the opposite sex, but no two had crushes on the same person.

- Frank liked the cheerleader but was sitting opposite the valedictorian.
- Gina was sitting next to the cheerleader and was crazy about the class president.
- Betty was in love with the person sitting opposite her.
- Joe, who was not the valedictorian, was sitting between the volleyball player and the class president.
- Ron disliked the basketball player.
- Sally, an orphan, was sitting against the wall and had a crush on the volleyball player.

- The volleyball player sat opposite the principal's child.

Identify each person's claim to fame.

Problems of this type are usually solved by a process of elimination. A matrix provides a way of organizing the information and keeping track of what has been eliminated. For example, after reading statement (1) above, it is clear that Frank is not the cheerleader or the valedictorian. In the matrix below, with rows labeled by names and columns by fames, we place an X in the intersection of the row labeled Frank and the columns labeled Cheerleader and Valedictorian. This indicates that Frank cannot be either the cheerleader or the valedictorian. Similarly, from statement (2), Gina cannot be either the cheerleader or the class president and we place an X in the intersection of the appropriate boxes.

	Cheerleader	Valedictorian	President	Volleyball	Basketball	Principal's Child
Betty						
Frank	X	X				
Gina	X		X			
Joe						
Ron						
Sally						

You may also find it useful to draw a seating chart for the booth, before continuing on with your elimination to solve the problem. Such pictures are often helpful, as we discuss next.

Pictures and Graphs

Creating a picture or a graph of the information in a problem provides a concrete way of displaying the facts and manipulating the relationships that the problem describes. The following examples help illustrate the utility of pictures and graphs in solving problems.

Pie in the Face

In a TV Game Show Contest, in order to win a prize, a contestant must run to a table, pick up a cream pie, race toward a partner and give him or her a face full of pie in the quickest time possible. Mary and Bill decided that since Mary is faster than Bill, she would do the running. They also felt that the shortest distance traveled would yield the quickest time. The table is 13 feet long and is filled with chocolate cream pies. Mary is standing 5 feet away from the end of the table and perpendicular to it. Similarly, Bill is 8 feet from the opposite end of the table and perpendicular to it. What is the shortest distance Mary must travel to accomplish this feat?

Solving this problem without the aid of a picture is difficult. The figure below, not only helps you visualize the situation, but also creates the opportunity to add and manipulate information. Try solving the problem with this hint: What if the table becomes a line and Bill stands on the opposite side of it? If the hint doesn't help, get some props - a piece of string for example – and make some measurements.

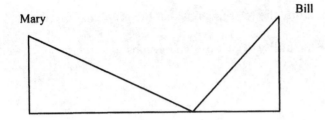

Mary   Bill

Scheduling Speakers

A symposium on teaching is being sponsored by the University of Connecticut. Six speakers are scheduled to speak- call them A, B, C, D, E and F. The university decides on four time slots: (1) 9-10, (2) 10-11, (3) 11-12, and (4) 1-2 with an hour lunch break from 12 to 1. A poll among the faculty indicated that some of the speakers are especially popular and should not speak at the same time. An X marked in the column and row in the matrix given below indicates which speakers should not speak simultaneously. For example, A should not speak at the same time as B, D or F. Find an arrangement for the speakers given the time slots and the additional information that speaker E will speak in the afternoon only.

	A	B	C	D	E	F

A		X		X		X
B	X			X		X
C					X	
D	X	X				X
E			X			
F	X	X		X		

Drawing a graph of the information given in the chart above may organize your work and suggest an approach to the problem. For example, let each speaker be represented by a point. We can construct a graph of the situation as follows. First, randomly arrange the points on paper. Next, connect two points provided the two speakers represented by the points should not speak at the same time as indicated in the chart. (Complete the figure below.)

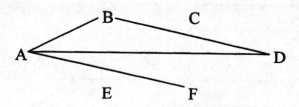

We can now assign time slots as follows. Since speaker E must speak in the afternoon we should assign her the time slot between 1-2 (i.e., time slot 4) and record this on our graph by putting (4) next to point E (see graph below). Next, since there is no line connecting speakers A and E they can speak at the same time. So, let's assign speaker A to time slot 4 and record this information in our graph. Moving to speaker B, we see that speakers A and B should not speak at the same time. Therefore, we assign a different time slot to speaker B, that is, let's assign speaker B to the first time slot (i.e., between 9-

10) and record this on our graph. Continuing on in this fashion, you should be able to assign each speaker to an appropriate time slot and record your results in a solution table.

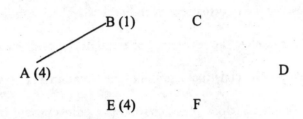

Time Slots	Speakers
9 - 10	
10 - 11	
11 - 12	
1 - 2	

Are there other ways to arrange the speakers in the given time slots? If so, give a different arrangement.

Models

Sometimes creating a physical model of a situation can provide a perspective to a problem that is not apparent in a picture. Perhaps you used this method to help with the *Pie in the Face* problem by using string. The *Heap of Beans* problem also showed how a model (real beans) helped to provide insight. Here's another example.

A goat is tied to one of the corners of a

rectangular barn on a rope that is 50 feet long.

The dimensions of the barn are 40 feet by 30

feet. Assuming that the goat can graze

wherever its rope allows it to reach, what is

the square footage of the grazing area for the goat?

$L \times W = sq\ ft.$

Drawing an accurate picture (see figure below) of this is a promising way to begin.

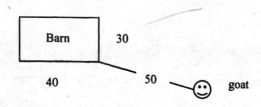

Although this drawing is helpful, creating a physical model of the situation may reveal

information not found in the 2-dimensional figure. For example, construct a box

proportional to the length and width given in the problem. Next, take a length of string

(again, in correct proportion), knot it on the inside of the box and pull it taut through a

hole in one corner of the box. Tie a pencil to the end of the string. Place the box on a

large piece of paper and holding the rope tight move the pencil around the barn. The

sketched area represents a model of the area the goat can graze. (See figure below.)

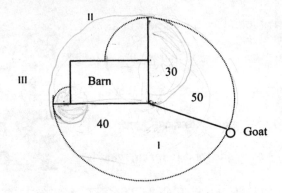

The figure shows three regions (I, II, III) where the goat can graze. Region I represents an area three-fourths of a circle whose radius is 50 feet. Regions II and III represent areas given by one-fourth of a circle whose radii are 10' and 20' respectively. With this information you should be able to solve the problem.

Mental Images

Written and spoken ideas become more meaningful if we can form a mental image to go along with what we are reading or hearing. The importance of such images is easy to illustrate. Read the next paragraph through once quickly.

> *A seashore is a better place than the street. At first it is better to run than to walk. You may have to try several times. It takes some skill but it's easy to learn. Even young children can have fun. Once you're successful, complications are minimal. Birds seldom get too close. Too many people doing the same thing, however, can cause problems. One needs lots of room. Beware of rain; it ruins everything. If there are no complications, it can be very peaceful. A rock will serve as an anchor. If things break loose from it, however, you will not get a second chance.*

Each sentence makes sense by itself, but if you haven't played the game before, the paragraph doesn't hang together - it leaves you confused. Go back and reread it now with the additional information that it deals with *kite flying*.

Pause and reflect on why the paragraph made more sense the second time. Wasn't it because you could form a nice mental image of flying kites at the beach? This exercise should convince you of the power of forming pictures in your mind as you go about problem solving. As you read a problem over, try to mentally place it into a setting you are familiar with. Does it talk about driving a car at 50 miles and hour? You can picture yourself in your own red Mercedes, driving down the highway at 50.

As another example of the power of visualization, a research study (DeFranco and Curcio, [10]) asked 6th grade students to review the following solved problem:

Bus Trip. We have 328 senior citizens going on a trip. A bus can seat 40 people. How many buses are needed so that all the senior citizens can go on the trip?

Answer: 328÷40 is 8 with a remainder of 8, or 8 1/5 buses.

In responding to this work, only 2 students out of 20 recognized that there is no such thing as a "fifth of a bus" and said the answer should be 9 buses. Approximately one month later the same students were given a similar problem to solve, but this time were asked to call for the buses using a phone provided by the researchers. In this instance, 16 out of the 20 students interpreted the remainder correctly and gave a feasible response. It was clear that when given the problem in an authentic setting, the students were able to make sense of and use mathematics in an appropriate manner. You can provide your own "authentic setting" by using suitable mental images – See the senior citizens getting on the bus.

Try this imaging on the *Acrobats* problem below, along with pictures and charts and your other rapidly developing problem-solving skills.

Acrobats

You are the manager of a troupe of acrobats. Each of your acrobats wears an outfit consisting of a top and tights. Both the tops and tights come in blue, red and yellow and each acrobat wears a different color scheme (top and tights). If all possible combinations appear (and none are repeated), how many acrobats are in the troupe?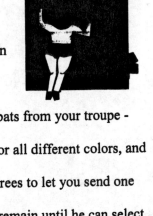

Next, the king wants to hire a *royal team* of acrobats from your troupe - three acrobats wearing tops that are all the same or all different colors, and tights that are all the same or all different. He agrees to let you send one acrobat at a time to the throne room, where they remain until he can select a royal team from the acrobats gathered there. If he pays you $100 for each acrobat you send over, how much money can you make?

Can you See the acrobats in their different costumes? In your mind, play a video of yourself sending them over to the throne room one at a time. Each time you send an acrobat, the king sends back $100. What is the maximum number of $100 bills you can collect by a careful selection of the acrobats you send?

Memorization

I (one of the authors) went to my first school open house shortly after my daughter began kindergarten. At the front door I encountered the school principal greeting parents. "Who's your child?" he asked. "Rebecca Vinsonhaler." To my amazement, he then replied "You must be Charles and this is your wife Patricia." When I expressed surprise that he knew our names, the principal revealed that he knew the names of all 350 students in the school along with their parents. In most cases he could give the address and phone number as well!

I have always had trouble remembering names, so I begged him for the secret of his astounding achievement. He paused, as if reluctant to share the treasure. "You know," he said, "I just make it important." He went on to describe a few of his techniques, like going straight to the family folder if he ever forgot a name. But basically his method was to Be Proactive, to engage the problem with all his resources. You can use his secret to study for exams, become accomplished at recalling names, or memorizing telephone numbers from the phone book. To help you along, we'll look at a technique that falls under the See It heading, a spin-off of a classic nursery rhyme that helps you associate a visual image with something you want to memorize. Here's how it works. First you learn the following ditty:

One is a bun,

Two is a shoe,

Three is a tree,

Four is a door,

Five is a hive,

Six is sticks,

Seven is heaven,

Eight is a gate,

Nine is a line,

Ten is a hen.

Then, when you are given a list of at most 10 items to memorize (for more than 10 you can add verses, "Eleven is Kevin," for example), you associate to each item in your list a picture that ties into the corresponding verse in the ditty. For example, suppose you wanted to remember the following items on a grocery list:

> 1-milk
> 2-bread
> 3-oranges
> 4-lettuce
> 5-hot dogs
> 6-apple juice
> 7-yogurt
> 8-wine
> 9-ice cream
> 10-napkins

For the first word, *milk*, you might form a mental picture of a glass of milk and a cinnamon bun sitting on a table (since from our ditty, One is a bun). For the second word, *bread*, you could imagine a loaf of bread sticking out the top of a boot (for Two is a shoe). Go through the list quickly, taking about 5 seconds to associate an image with each item and corresponding verse. Then have a friend ask you some questions about your list of items – what was number 6?, which number was *ice cream*? and so on. You may be amazed at how easy it is to come up with the answers and how long you retain the list in your memory.

Visualization.

> *I skate to where I think the puck will be.*

> ---Wayne Gretsky

The forming of mental images can affect the future as well as the present. Over the past 50 years, a number of books, *The Power of Positive* 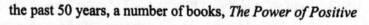 *Thinking, Psycho Cybernetics, Peak Performance, The Seven* 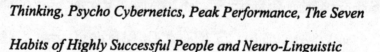 *Habits of Highly Successful People and Neuro-Linguistic Programming* have extolled the virtues of affirmative thought. Near the end of a tight football game, a good coach doesn't tell the running back, "Don't fumble." Instead he says, "Hold onto the ball," putting a positive image into the player's mind. If you've played much golf, you'll know a golfer (maybe yourself) who says, "You don't want to slice it into the pond over there on the right," and proceeds to do just that. You give yourself a much better chance by imagining your drive hooking gently to the left center of the fairway - before you step up to stroke it. The same principles apply to achieving any important goal, from making an A in a math course to giving up smoking cigarettes. With an important exam coming up, tell yourself "I'm doing all the studying necessary to make an A on my exam."

Avoid negative thoughts like, "If I don't do well on this exam, I'm really in trouble."

Here's a simple exercise to help you try out this important idea of visualization.

Achievement Scene

Take a few minutes to think of an important goal that you would like to attain

within the next few months. It can be any kind of goal - academic, personal, athletic.

Take a piece of paper and at the top, describe as best you can <u>in one sentence</u> what your

goal is. Underneath write, "Achievement Scene." Then, using the present tense and in as

much detail as possible, describe the moment you realize your goal. Put in sights, sounds,

smells, all the sensations you will experience at the moment your goal is attained, always

in the present tense, as if it is happening this moment. Don't forget to acknowledge the

people who helped you, along with your own sacrifices. If you wish, you can add

symbols or sketches that are meaningful to you. When you have completed the

description, write below it "I am doing all I need to do to realize this in harmony and

gratitude." Then place your scene someplace where you will see it frequently, over your

desk, on the table by your bed. Even if you stick it in a drawer, you may be amazed by

the subtle power of "seeing" your goal realized even as you set out to achieve it. (Note: A

basketball player in one of our problem-solving classes described an achievement scene

in which his team won a national championship. Five months later, he helped the

University of Connecticut beat Duke in the finals of the NCAA tournament.)

Clear Writing = Clear Thinking.

We believe that clear writing and clear thinking go hand-in-hand. What does this have to do with problem solving? First, if you can't write a clear explanation of your solution to a problem, then you probably don't understand the solution as well as you think. You may not even have a solution at all. Second, if you can't explain your solution to someone else, you severely limit the effectiveness of your work. Many real-life problems are solved *by* groups *for* groups. Clear communication is essential. Fear of writing is just as common as "math anxiety," but both can be overcome. You can learn to relish the refinement and insight that comes with putting your thoughts on paper. But you need to be proactive, of course. Clear writing = clear thinking.

Clear Writing Activity. Write a letter to a friend or relative explaining how to win the game *A Heap of Beans*. Assume your reader has never played the game before.

Suggested Stretches: *8 - 15*

Suggested Projects: *Commuter, Different Angle, Grilled Cheese, Largest Lake, Neighbor Knockout, Parking Lot, Percolation, Symmetry, Three Squares, Weights*

Chapter 5

SIMPLIFY IT

There is a master key to success with which no man can fail. Its name is simplicity. Simplicity, I mean, in the sense of reducing to the simplest possible terms every problem that besets us.

--- Sir Henri Deterding

...the source of all great mathematics is the special case, the concrete example. It is frequent in mathematics that every instance of a concept of seemingly great generality is in essence the same as a small and concrete special case.

--- Paul Halmos

Many of the problems we encounter in our lives appear complex and difficult to solve. Sometimes solving a problem becomes easier if we break it up into smaller more manageable subproblems. For example, planning a wedding can be an overwhelming task but by attending to individual details of the wedding (e.g., the wedding hall, the band, the caterer, etc.) one at a time, the task becomes more manageable.

In a similar way, mathematicians use simplifying techniques to solve difficult and complex problems. For example, when faced with a problem, mathematicians usually begin by examining individual and/or special cases of the problem and then look for a pattern to generalize their results. By examining simpler, and sometimes more concrete cases of a problem, mathematicians gain insight into a problem and ways to approach the problem. As usual, we illustrate with examples.

Try Simple Cases and Look for a Pattern.

Changing Places

On a strip with 11 squares, there are 5 quarters placed heads up on the first 5 squares and 5 quarters placed tails up on the last 5 squares. The allowable moves are to move a coin one step forward (toward the opposite end) into an empty space and to hop over an opposing coin into an empty space. No backward moves or double jumps are allowed. (It might help if we See the problem by making a picture.)

H	H	H	H	H		T	T	T	T	T

Try playing the game now. Unless you are much sharper than average, you'll become gridlocked in relatively few moves. How can we Simplify this game? One possibility is to play with fewer coins. Try a version with one H and one T on a three-square strip.

H		T

Easy isn't it? Now try it with two H's and two T's on five-square strip.

H	H		T	T

As you work through these simple cases, you will eventually see a pattern that helps you solve the original problem and even more complicated versions. Research has indicated that problem solvers are more successful and take less time if they work through simple cases before tackling the main problem. So whenever you encounter a problem for which there is an easier version, *Try a Simple Case.*

Handshakes

In a train station waiting room you find yourself waiting for the train along with 15 other travelers. Everyone in the room decides that it is a good idea to become acquainted by shaking hands with everyone else in the room. How many handshakes will take place?

In a problem involving large numbers, good problem solvers routinely start with a similar problem that uses small numbers (e.g., 1, 2, etc.) instead. Working with small numbers and investigating cases helps to make the problem concrete and usually provides some insight into the problem. Often a pattern develops that leads to a solution, not only of the original problem, but much more complicated ones.

In the Handshake problem, instead of trying to solve this problem with 16 people (why 16?) in the room, begin by assuming you were the only person in the room. How many handshakes would take place? The question is a bit silly and the answer obvious, but it provides a starting point and makes the problem more concrete. So, for one person in the room we know that zero handshakes take place. What if there were two people in the room? Once again the answer is obvious--one handshake would take place. What if there were three people in the room? This time an easy calculation tells you that three handshakes occur. How many handshakes would take place with four people in the room? By now you have learned that a picture or graph can be helpful. For this problem, draw a picture with the letters A, B, C, and D representing the four people and a line connecting each pair of letters where a handshake takes place. For example, since person A shakes hands with person B we indicate this on our graph with a line from A to B. Finishing the graph we see that with four people in a room, six handshakes take place.

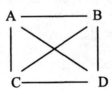

In a similar way, with five people in the room, ten handshakes would occur.. How many new handshakes are added with each additional person? A table can help you keep track of the information—fill in the table below to solve the problem.

Number of People in the Room	Number of Handshakes
1	0
2	1
3	3
4	6
5	10
6	
7	
8	
9	
10	
11	
12	
13	
14	
15	
16	

Can you recognize a pattern with respect to the Number of People in the Room and the Number of Handshakes that take place? How many handshakes would take place if there were 25 people in the room?

Telescoping Sums

What is the sum of the following series

$$\frac{1}{1\times 2} + \frac{1}{2\times 3} + \frac{1}{3\times 4} + ... + \frac{1}{100\times 101}?$$

It would be very time consuming to add up each of the 100 terms (why 100?) to arrive at the answer. To examine simple cases, let's start with just one term, that is, 1/(1×2). The sum of the first term is 1/2. What is the sum of the first and second terms? That's an easy calculation, 1/2 + 1/6 = 2/3. What is the sum of the first three terms? 1/2 + 1/6 + 1/12 = 2/3 + 1/12 = 9/12 = 3/4. What is the sum of the first three terms? 3/4 + 1/20 = 16/20 = 4/5. Once again, let's record our results in a table and look for a pattern.

Term	Sum
1	1/2
2	1/2 + 1/6 = 2/3
3	1/2 + 1/6 + 1/12 = 3/4

Can you recognize a pattern with respect to the term and the sum? What is the sum of the first 100 terms? Can you guess a formula that would give the sum for any number of terms in this series?

Now try the next two problems—remember to examine simpler cases and look for a pattern in order to answer each question. Create a table to record your results.

Candy Conundrum

In how many different ways can 3 children divide 20 pieces of candy so that each child gets at least one piece of candy?

Factorials

How many zeros appear at the end of 100! (Note: 100! = (100)(99)(98)••••(1), the product of the integers from 1 to 100.)

Make Assumptions

Many problems, as we have noted, are disturbingly vague. We can Simplify them by making assumptions, plugging in numbers, Seeing examples. The next problem is a prime candidate for this technique.

The Commuter. A commuter rides the train to and from work each day. Her husband meets her at the train station and drives her home. One day the commuter leaves work early, catches a different train and arrives at the station one hour ahead of schedule. It being a nice day, she decides to walk toward home.

Somewhere along the way she meets her husband, driving from home to pick her up at the usual time. She gets in the car and they drive back, arriving 20 minutes earlier than normal. How long was the commuter walking?

This problem appears difficult since it seems like too little information is given. How fast does the woman walk? How far away from home is the train station? Here's a chance to Be Proactive, to "move toward activity. We resolve to give this problem our best shot.

Let's start by trying to See It. A sketch might be helpful.

| Train Station | | Home |

This picture is a little bare. We need more information about the problem. Maybe we can Simplify it by making assumptions, putting in some numbers to make things more concrete. What time does the wife usually arrive at the station? Five o'clock seems reasonable. How long does the drive home take? The problem doesn't say - let's try 30 minutes. Now the picture looks like this:

Train Station		Home

5:00 →   5:30

What about when the wife arrives at the station an hour early? The problem says she arrives home 20 minutes earlier than normal, which would be 5:10. We can add another row to our picture for this information.

Train Station		Home

5:00 (normal) →   5:30 (normal arrival)

4:00 (early)   →   5:10 (early)

How else can we Stir It Up? We haven't thought much about the husband yet? What does his afternoon look like? To pick up the wife as usual, he would leave the house at 4:30 pm for the 30-minute drive to the station. We'll add that information to our picture.

Train Station		Home

5:00 (normal) →   5:30 (normal arrival)

4:00 (early)   →   5:10 (early)

                  ←   4:30 (normal departure)

Now is a good time to **Pause and Reflect** - where are we, where do we want to go? A short mental video shows the husband leaving the house as usual, meeting his wife on the road, turning around and driving home. His trip takes 20 minutes less than usual, 40 minutes instead of an hour in our scenario. Aha! That means he drives 20 minutes in each direction, so that he meets his wife at 4:50. We'll add this insight to our chart.

Train Station		Home

5:00 (normal) →		5:30 (normal arrival)
4:00 (early) →		5:10 (early)
	⬆ 🚗 ←	4:30 (normal departure)
	4:50	

With the information in front of us, we may conclude that the wife walked 50 minutes, from 4:00 to 4:50.

Let's **Pause and Reflect** again. Is our answer reasonable? Did we make any assumptions that affected the answer? One way to address these questions, as well as test our understanding of the solution, is to work through the problem with different assumptions. For example,

- Change the normal arrival time at the train station to 5:30 and the normal driving time to 20 minutes. Do you still get the same answer?

- Change the time saved by walking to 10 minutes instead of 20. Then 30 minutes, 40 minutes. Do you see a pattern? Put your information in two columns to help See It.

Here is another problem where making assumptions is essential.

Parking Lot

 You pull into the mall on a Saturday shopping trip only to find all the spaces full. Instead of driving around looking for a parking spot, you poise your car at the end of a row, commanding 16 spaces. As soon as one of those 16 spaces opens up, you will get to park. How long do you expect to wait?

Whoa! How can we solve this problem? We aren't given enough information. Well, we've learned to be **Proactive**, so let's plunge in. We can **See** the problem by drawing a row with 16 parking spaces and our red Mercedes poised at the end. Next, we can **Simplify** the problem by supposing that there is only one space. Now we could make an assumption and draw on experience and make a guess, say 10 minutes to wait for the one space to open up. Another approach is to make some assumptions about the shoppers. We can assume that the average shopper spends about one hour in the mall on a Saturday (is this reasonable?). If that is the case, then how long do we expect to wait for our one space to open up? We could wait one second if the owner comes out immediately, or we could wait one hour (on average) if the owner has just gone into the mall. It seems logical to guess that the space will become available somewhere between these two extremes and we might as well guess the middle - 1/2 hour. So, for one space we wait 30 minutes. How about two spaces? Solve this simple case and continue on to build up to the solution of the original (16 spaces) problem.

Here are some additional problems where simplification is possible, in particular by making assumptions. These are complicated conundrums and for now you don't need to solve them. Just describe ways in which you might simplify each one.

- Solve the parking problem on your campus.

- What would you do if you won the lottery?

- Determine the volume of Madison Square Garden.

- Find the surface area of Lake Michigan.

- Translate *Parking Lot* into a problem involving waiting in a bank or a restaurant. Then Simplify in some way.

- Determine the number of packages you would recommend for an *express line* in a supermarket.

A final caution. Einstein said "Everything should be made as simple as possible, but not simpler." Alfred North Whitehead's version was "Seek simplicity, and distrust it." Their point is that our strategy, Simplify It, while powerful, can mislead the overzealous user. Some Pause and Reflection is recommended when applying the solution of a simplified problem to the original.

Suggested Stretches: *16 - 24*

Suggested Projects: *Forty Thieves, Graphs, Inequality, Lease or Buy, Nim, Percolation, Pearls, Planetary Voyage, Seven Elevators, Trouble With Tribbles*

Chapter 6

STIR IT UP

What we have to learn to do, we learn by doing.

---Aristotle

In this chapter we will discuss some ways to "get your hands dirty," to put your spoon into the problem stew and churn—that is, Stir It Up.

Trial and Error.

This is a classic way to solve problems, to guess and check - try different answers until you come up with the right one. For some types of problems, this is the only way to solve them.

Cryptarithmetic

What would you make of this addition problem?

```
    E    L    F
+   E    L    F
-----------------
F   O    O    L
```

The rules are easy. Each letter represents a distinct digit from 0 to 9. That is, every time the letter F appears it stands for the same single digit number. We never put a

0 at the beginning of a number. The problem is to find values for the letters so that the sum makes sense.

We can use some properties of addition, but basically we just start guessing and checking. The letter F appears three times, once all by itself on the bottom line. What could it be? The rules say it can't be 0. What about 1? That's possible (how?). What about 2? The biggest E could be is 9 and $9 + 9 = 18$. What this shows is that we can "carry" at most 1 to the next column when we add two digits, so F could not be 2 or larger. OK, so F = 1. That makes L = 2 and therefore O = 4. Finally, we must have E = 7 (why?). Thus the addition problem becomes

```
      7   2   1
  +   7   2   1
  ─────────────
  1   4   4   2
```

Here we had little choice but to use trial and error, keeping in mind the special features of the problem. It is a method that works in a wide variety of situations. Many times guessing will solve a problem that you might think needed much more sophisticated techniques.

Ages

Amy is 10 years older than Bill. In 5 years she will be twice as old. What are their two ages?

The way we learned to do this problem is to let x be Amy's age, y be Bill's age and so on. That will work, but let's see how easy it is to just guess an answer. Amy is 10 years older than Bill, so we could try Amy 30, Bill 20. In 5 years we'll have Amy 35 and Bill 25. That doesn't make Amy twice as old as Bill, so we need to make another guess. You finish the problem. How many guesses did it take? The next problem might take a few more guesses.

Grandfather

In 1996 my grandfather's age equaled the product of the four digits in the year he was born and the same was true for his daughter. Find the two birth years.

Warning: The next problem requires some Seeing. Chart <u>all</u> the possibilities.

Faculty Debts

The accountant complains to the mathematician: "I lent money to five faculty members and still haven't been paid back. You are one of them; the other four owe me 12 dollars altogether, but I don't remember how much each person owes me separately."

"Are the debts in whole dollars?"

"Yes. I do remember that the four other debts multiplied together

63

equals your debt. Do you remember how much you owe me?"

"Yes, but I still haven't figured out how much each of the other four owe you."

"Wait! The statistician is the one who owes the least."

"That does it. Now I know the amount of each debt."

If you were the mathematician, could you determine the amounts?

Experiment

Another way to stir the problem soup is to run an experiment that might give you information and insight. This next problem is an old one, but a few years ago Marilyn vos Savant, who owns the world's highest IQ, featured it in her newspaper column. She received letters from hundreds of people, many of them holding Ph.D.'s in mathematics, strongly defending each of two answers. The story is a striking illustration of the confusing nature of probability questions. As we will see, however, a simple experiment can do much to clear up the confusion.

Should You Switch?

You are a contestant on a game show where one million dollars is hidden behind one of three closed doors. There is nothing behind either of the other two doors. You guess door 1, but before opening that door the game show host opens door 2 and shows you that nothing was hidden there. He offers you the chance to switch your guess to door 3. Should you switch?

The two most common answers are "Yes", you should switch, or "It doesn't make any difference." Try this experiment with a friend to see if it helps you gain insight into the problem. Sit in two chairs with your backs facing each other. In Round 1 your friend will be the game show host and you will be the contestant. Your friend will put a 1,2 or 3 on a piece of paper and ask you to guess which digit she chose. After you guess (say you guess 1), she will tell you one of the other two digits that is not the answer (say she tells you 2 wasn't it) and offer you the chance to switch your guess (in this case, to 3). Play this game 10 times in Round 1, with you the contestant choosing NOT to switch each time. Keep track of the number of times (out of 10) that you win the money. Now switch roles - you become the game show host, and play the game 10 more times. In Round 2 your friend, the contestant, will choose to SWITCH each time. Keep track of how many times (out of 10) that she wins the money.

Based on this experiment, how would you answer the Should You Switch question? Did the experiment give you any insight? Can you See how you win with the Switch strategy as opposed to the No Switch strategy? If not, try the experiment again, keeping in mind the question of how you win in each case. After that, if the answer still isn't clear, Ask Questions. Try a version of the game where there are 10 doors and the host opens 8 of them!

Shed The Cocoon.

Oftentimes it is difficult to begin a problem, perhaps because we wrap ourselves

 in a cocoon of inhibitions, misconceptions and prejudices. In this section we examine some ways to burst these bonds. You may have seen other names for the ideas described here, such as brainstorming, lateral thinking, or conceptual blockbusting. One of the most common mistakes we problem-solvers are guilty of is putting unnecessary constraints on our efforts to solve a problem. We all have the fear of looking stupid, of failing. It's much easier to criticize someone else's idea than to put one of our own on the table. Shed the cocoon, let go, treat yourself to the luxury of stirring up ideas out of that marvelous brain of yours without worrying about what someone else thinks, or what is "not allowed." Here are two specific ways to open the idea faucet.

Talk First, Then Think

The development of mental skills often demands that we first express out loud things that we later process silently. Some scholars even argue that silent conscious reflection itself required a long period of evolution. They conjecture that initially all thoughts were spoken aloud and heard by the thinker himself, who would then give a verbal response just as if someone else had spoken. Verbalizing your thoughts on a problem, no matter how bizarre they might seem, can kick-start your own problem solving engine, your amazing brain, and do the same for everyone around you.

Think Quantity

In the beginning of a brainstorming session, the important goal is to generate a lot of ideas, not just "good" ones. Even the most absurd sounding suggestion can trigger a connection that will lead to the solution of a problem. Alex Osborn, one of the pioneers of brainstorming, said "Quantity! and more quantity! is the order of the day." A well-known example of brainstorming success involved a group of executives at the Gillette Company. In order to develop a new shampoo, they pretended that they were shafts of hair! In this state of mind, they threw out ideas about what a hair shaft would want the most – strong but gentle cleansing, etc. By the end of the session the executives agreed that what they wanted was a shampoo that would adapt to every type of hair. The product that resulted, Silkience, became one of the most popular shampoos on the market.

People are reticent about voicing their thoughts. By focusing on generating a large number of ideas, we can burst out of our inhibiting cocoon and achieve surprising results. Let's try some examples.

Eraser

In five minutes, write down all the uses you can think of for a pink eraser.

Light Switches.

You are standing at the end of a long hallway where there are three standard light switches on the wall. At the other end of the hall is a room with a closed door. Inside the room there is a lamp that is controlled by one of the switches. You are

allowed one trip down the hall into the room, but you must close the door when you return. How do you determine which switch controls the lamp?

Magic Cuts.

Cut the table in three pieces, along the lines to get equal totals on each piece. One cut is shown at the right. Can you find another, and possibly even a third?

2	5	6
9	1	8
4	3	7

2	5	6
9	1	8
4	3	7

Hint: It helps to See this problem from a different viewpoint.

Work Backwards

A final Stirring technique is to begin at the end of a problem and work backwards. In working backwards on a problem you begin with the goal of the problem and ask yourself the question, "What do I need to know or do mathematically to arrive at this last step of the problem?" Once you've answered that question you continue to ask the same question until you arrive at the answer to the problem. If a problem must be solved in stages, it is often easiest to start with the last stage instead of the first. Visualize yourself on the last step, then think about the immediately preceding step, and so on.

Die Hard III

You have a 4-quart container and a 9-quart container and an unlimited supply of water. How do you measure *exactly* 6 quarts?

It seems to help to imagine yourself, standing proudly, holding exactly six quarts in one of the containers. What did you do just prior to obtaining six quarts?

Checkerboard Chase. (Mason, Burton & Stacey, [20])

Player A begins by placing a checker on the lower left-hand corner of a

checkerboard (8 by 8 squares). Player B places a checker one square to the right or one square up or one square diagonally up and to the right of Player A's checker. Then A places a checker one square to the right or one square up or one square diagonally up and to the right of Player B. The players continue alternating moves in this way. The winner is the player who places a checker in the upper right corner. Would you rather be Player A or Player B?

The winning player places a checker in the upper right corner. What did the previous move look like? Work backwards.

Analogous Problems

An important way of stirring up a problem, emphasized by Polya [24] and others, is to try and recall a related problem or a simpler analogous problem to the one you are trying to solve. Recalling how you solved a similar problem to the one you are being asked to solve is a very effective way to begin a problem! To practice this strategy, see if you can find a connection between *Checkerboard Chase* and the problem *Two Bean Heaps* (with 8 beans in each heap). What about Stretches 27 and 29?

Suggested Stretches: *25 - 57*

Suggested Projects: *Cryptarithmetic, Judge, Largest Lake, Pick's Theorem, Polyominoes, Seven Elevators, Stacking Rulers, Symmetry, True or False, Weights*

Chapter 7

PAUSE AND REFLECT

One of the hallmarks of good problem solvers ... is that, while they are in the midst of working problems, such individuals seem to maintain an internal dialogue regarding the way that their solutions evolve. Plans are made, they are evaluated and contrasted with other plans.... Solutions are monitored and assessed "on line" and signs of trouble suggest that current approaches might be terminated and others considered.... one might say that part of competent problem solvers' control behavior is that they argue with themselves as they work.

--- A. Schoenfeld

Mother Theresa once said at the start of a busy day, "I have so much to do today that I'm going to spend two hours in prayer instead of one." Her problem-solving technique is perhaps the most universal of our PSSSP five, **P**ause and Reflect. Reflection is defined as "serious thought, the fixing of the mind on some subject." It is recommended at the beginning a problem, at the end when you have obtained an answer, and throughout the solution process as you proactively apply your **SSS**kills. Often there is no clear division in the stages of a problem solution, so your reflecting will depend on where you are going as well as where you have been.

In The Beginning

Reflect first on the problem. Do you understand it? What is the unknown? What is the goal of the problem? What are the conditions of the problem? Do I have enough information to solve the problem? What should the answer look like? Can you recall a similar problem? Can you See the problem more clearly? Can it be Simplified? What will you use to Stir with? Understanding the problem and reviewing your problem-solving troopSSS are critical if you want to develop an effective plan. One technique you can use to see if you understand the problem is to explain it to a friend.

As an exercise, reflect on each of the following three problems. You don't need to solve them right now, just write a few sentences indicating that you understand the problem and explaining how you plan to solve it.

Multiple Locks

You belong to a Math Club that has accumulated valuable jewelry (gold pens, platinum protractors, etc.). The treasure is kept in a chest. For security reasons, you want at least two of your 10 club members present  when the chest is open. To insure this, you put multiple locks on the chest and distribute keys to members so that no one member can open the chest, but any two members can. Each lock has a different key, but you can make several copies of the same key to distribute to the club members. What is the fewest number of locks and keys that you will need?

Jumping Frogs

How many ways can a frog hop up a twelve-step staircase if he can hop either one or two steps on each hop?

Dating Service

A dating service has as clients 6 recently divorced couples. Each client wants the opportunity to socialize with the other clients of the opposite sex, but refuses to be in the same room as his or her ex-spouse. The service wants to throw a sequence of parties to bring people together. They want each male and female pair to attend some party (not necessarily as a couple), but of course no formerly married couple should attend the same party. Is it possible to do this? If so, what is the fewest number of parties that can be held? What are all the possible sequences that have the fewest number of parties?

Having taken the time to reflect on these problems, you should be more prepared to solve them effectively. We now discuss some suggestions for reflection during the solution process.

In The Middle

Even with a good plan of attack, you may not prevail immediately. In that case there is usually benefit in **Pausing and Reflecting**. As we immerse ourselves in a problem and begin swimming about, it is easy to forget why we got wet in the first place. Skilled problem solvers constantly check to see that they are headed in the right direction—that is, they *Monitor their progress* while solving a problem. The ability to monitor one's progress in the midst of solving a problem is a key component for success. By monitoring your work you may realize that your original approach or plan may or may not be appropriate or it may lead to a decision to change or to select a strategy to try on a problem. Making notes on mistakes as well as insights gained while working on a problem prevent time-wasting backtracking. Remember to write STUCK! and YES! in the appropriate spots to keep from becoming overly frustrated and to reward yourself for a good idea.

Sometimes the best thing you can do with a problem is to put it aside—that is, *Sleep on it*. In spite of your best efforts you end up in blind alleys and exasperation undermines your ability to choose a promising new direction. Stop and listen to music or take a walk in the woods. A good night's sleep can work wonders on your problem perspective. Even switching to another task for a time can let you recharge your batteries for one problem while working on another.

One of the best ways to clarify a problem is to *Share it* with someone else. Find a blackboard and explain the problem to a patient friend. You'll be surprised at how often a situation sorts itself out as you talk about it. In addition, your friend may be able contribute fresh insights or point out an obvious mistake that you have become blind to. Instead of a friend, you might seek out someone who has expertise in the area of your problem. The quickest way to get a correct answer is to ask someone who already knows it.

Go back now, and try to make some progress on the three problems above - Multiple Locks, Jumping Frogs and Dating Service. Monitor yourself by repeatedly checking with your original reflections and adding new ones as you go along. If you can, share the problem with a friend. Let it rest overnight and notice any fresh perspective you bring to it the next day.

In The End

Having solved at least part of a problem, you will benefit from looking back at what you did and what you learned. Studies show that next to active participation during the process, reflection at the end of the process is the most important component of learning. Can you solve any of the three problems above? Take some time now to write a brief reflection on a problem you have solved. Where could you have been more efficient? What have you learned that might help you solve problems in the future? How could you extend your solution to more complicated problems? Can you solve the problem using a different approach? If you change the conditions in the problem, can you solve the new version?

Sometimes a good idea can be used far beyond the original problem the idea was developed to solve. Think about how you might use your methods to solve a different version of the problem you have just conquered. In *Multiple Locks*, what if three members are needed to open the chest? In *Jumping Frogs*, what if the frog could hop one, two, or three steps? Make reflection a major part of your problem solving and you'll make yourself a major problem-solver.

Here are some additional problems. Be sure to Pause and Reflect as you proceed toward a solution.

Suggested Stretches: *58 - 73*

Suggested Exercises. *Dollar Auction, Dominoes, Finding Happiness, Grilled Cheese, Inequality, Judge, Ordinal Games, Seven Elevators*

Chapter 8

INTERPERSONAL PROBLEMS

The important thing is this: To be able at any moment to sacrifice what we are for what we could become.

---Charles DuBois

One of the most exciting viewpoints on the trail of problem solving is the overlook where you see the panorama of opportunities for using the basic concepts and techniques of PSSSP. Mathematicians aren't the only ones who tend to be introverts, to deal with problems by withdrawing from them. Learning how to apply problem-solving skills in your social interactions can make a remarkable change in the way you relate to other people.

Peonies (a true story)

Once I (CV) came home from work to find that my wife had let a neighbor dig up a row of peonies (these are flowers) that I had spent many hours cultivating and grooming. The peonies had formed a nice military row along the driveway, and made it a pleasure to drive up into the yard, especially when the deep pink blooms appeared in late spring. On the evening in question, it was obvious that the military row had lost a war – my garden lay in ruins. Furious, I yelled at my wife through the window, using language not protected by the First Amendment. At some point I realized my kids were listening too and that I had just finished teaching a problem-solving class, so I collected myself and went to sit on our stone wall. My wife came out to try to talk to me, but realized quickly that it wasn't time for that yet and went back inside. As I sat on the wall, the coolness of the rock on my legs seemed to soak the heat of anger out of me. I calmed down enough to join the family for a rather quiet dinner. The next morning I was able to discuss with my wife what had happened (a failure to communicate, naturally). We eventually replanted peonies together.

This story is typical of interpersonal problems in several ways. First, the issue (here it's peonies) is not usually of dire consequence. Second, the problem almost always involves some kind of communication breakdown. Third, solutions are easier to obtain once the heat of anger has dissipated. We will use this specific example to illustrate application of the PSSSP principles to dealing with personal problems. No doubt you can add ideas and examples from your own experience.

Be Proactive

The basic idea is familiar: *Take Responsibility* for your own problems. If *you* have a problem, it's *your* job to work toward a solution. Blaming someone else might make you feel better in the short term; and waiting for someone else to solve your problem doesn't take much effort. But neither of these methods has any long-term effectiveness. The best way to get a problem solved is to recognize it, own it, and move toward activity. In the example above, the ruined row of peonies was a problem for **me**

(CV). Here's another example where *Taking Responsibility* provides a firm basis from which to begin.

Often we hear students say, "My Statistics professor flunked me and now they won't let me graduate." The student who may have said that was not Being **Proactive**. He formed his statement so that his own role in the problem was completely eliminated. He should have been asked to rephrase the problem, taking responsibility with his words. He might have said, "I flunked my Statistics class and now I don't have enough credits to graduate." Note how the emphasis has changed from blaming others to owning the problem, an important first step in solving it. The pronoun "I" is used frequently in an honest statement of a problem, a point we emphasize again below. How would you reword these statements to be more **Proactive**?

Personal Problems

- My parents won't listen to me.

- My dorm is too noisy to study in.

- They didn't give me any of the classes I wanted.

- My girlfriend is too judgmental. She won't let me be myself.

- My boyfriend always goes out with the guys and leaves me at home alone.

Another related insight that falls in the Be **Proactive** category is to recognize an interpersonal conflict as *Just Another Problem*. All too often we view conflict with another as a war where the goal is winning. When I (CV) saw my peonies massacred, I felt like committing bodily harm. But that wouldn't solve the problem. We can remind ourselves that achieving a solution is more likely if we view the problem as an opportunity, an opportunity to employ our PSSSP skills. By saying, *Just Another Problem* we can assuage our fears and direct our energies down promising paths.

Pause and Reflect

We look at the second **P** next, because in personal relationships it is important to

do this early and often. Many times our response to a problem situation is a reaction rather than a thoughtful, effective response (see the peony example above). In the *Seven Habits of Highly Effective People*, Stephen Covey [8] talks about the interval between stimulus (e.g., ruined peonies) and response (e.g., shouting at spouse) that can be so important in dealing with a problem. In the peony incident, I (CV) did not take advantage of that interval. Similarly, if you call your professor an "unfair grader," her natural instinct may be to react, to strike back by calling you a "lazy student." In so doing, the professor has not made any progress toward solving the problem—a student who feels that he was not graded fairly. If the professor can quickly **Pause and Reflect**, say by the old trick of counting to 10, she may be able to respond in a much more constructive way, perhaps by asking why you feel the way you do.

A more general principle is to *Deal With Your Emotions First*. Develop a technique, like counting to 10, that helps you bring your (perfectly valid) emotions under control. Make it a method that is as personal to you as possible. For example, ever since the Great Peony War, I (CV) frequently tell myself to "Go Sit On A Wall." If I can catch myself in the interval between stimulus and anger, I try to go to a quiet place to cool off before confronting the problem head on.

Sometimes it is also useful to *Begin At The End* - what do you really want the outcome to be? What I (CV) really want instead of chastising my wife is to have my peonies back. Likewise, if the professor wants to get back at you for calling her an unfair grader, it won't be hard to obtain revenge. But what she really wants to happen is for you to be comfortable in her class so you can make the most of your opportunity to learn. We need to keep the end in mind as we embark on a search for a solution.

For each of the five numbered statements in *Personal Problems* above, indicate how you would *Begin at the End* - enunciate the solution goal in each case.

See It

There are many productive ways to apply this strategy in the context of interpersonal problems. Perhaps the most effective is to use your ears to help you "See." For example, *Listen With Understanding.* If you have a problem with someone else,

chances are that person "sees" the problem differently than you do. To Proactively seek a solution, you can start by listening carefully to the other side. Another of Covey's [8] Seven Habits is, "Seek first to understand, then to be understood." If you invest in listening carefully to someone else, he is much more likely to listen to you, and the problem is much more likely to be solved.

Do you want a better relationship with your partner (boyfriend, girlfriend, roommate, sibling)? Take the time to *visualize* what an ideal relationship would be like. You can create an *Achievement Scene* (see Chapter 4) around the goal of an improved relationship. The exercise of visualizing contributes to *Beginning at the End*, giving you a positive image to work toward as you grapple with the problem. The peony problem would have been solved sooner if I had been enough of a problem solver to immediately envision them blooming again.

Clear writing is clear thinking, and putting your feelings and thoughts about a personal problem on paper can help you See the problem in sharper focus. An *Achievement Scene* is one way to do this, but you can make a list, a chart, or just write an essay about how you feel and what you would like to change. *Writing it down* can be an effective way of *Dealing With Your Emotions* also. The act of putting your feelings on paper can put them into perspective, help you to realize that the end of the world is not at hand - life has just given you another problem to solve.

Simplify It

The ideas from Chapter 5 translate easily to personal problems. Don't try to solve a major problem all at once. Break it up into more manageable tasks, into *Small steps*. If your relationship with your parents has you plotting mayhem, look for little things YOU can do to make things better. Find a common ground, a movie or a game of golf, where you can begin to improve the way you and your parents relate to each other. *Stick to the point.* If the immediate problem is the fact that they won't lend you the car, don't drag in how they used to be so restrictive when you were in high school, or the time they made you take ballroom dancing lessons. It's easy to drag in old issues when confronting new ones. Avoid this trap and *Stick to the point.*

Stir It Up

As you begin churning out ideas for solving the problem, *Think win-win.* Usually in the solution of a problem between two people, you never wind up with a winner and a loser. You either get two winners or two losers. Go into the process with the idea that you can find a solution that improves life for both of you. Working together you may find a better outcome than either of you imagined in the first place.

Finally, when you present YOUR problem to the other person(s) involved, *Say the right thing.* There are many ways to increase the effectiveness of discourse with others. Maintain good posture and eye contact, speak with a clear voice. As noted above, you will want to use the pronoun "**I**" frequently because you will be describing YOUR problem. "I feel angry when I come back to the apartment after a long day at school and find the kitchen filled with dirty dishes. I was wondering how we might address the problem." Along with honesty, you can make your points more palatable by using *Affirmation and Humor.* Compliments and appropriate jokes can soften the blow of a complaint and help you work together toward solving the problem.

Here are some exercises to test your understanding of the ideas in this chapter.

Evening Engagement

John slumped into the kitchen at the end of a long day of work. "Why don't things ever go smoothly," he moaned.

"Why don't you ever come home with a smile on your face?" snapped Martha.

"Maybe I would if I didn't have to look at the big dent you put in the Mercedes last month," retorted John.

Martha took a deep breath and counted to three. "I'm glad to see you, honey," she said. "Can we start over?"

Discuss how each of the PSSSP points described in this chapter were used, or could have been used in this evening engagement.

My Stuff

Describe an interpersonal problem from your own experience. Use fictitious characters if you wish. Then tell how the PSSP techniques were used or could have been used to help solve the problem.

Mission Statement

Winnie the Pooh once said:

How can you get very far

If you don't know Who you are?

How can you do what you ought,

If you don't know What you've got?

And if you don't know Which to do

Of all the things in front of you,

Then what you'll have when you are through

Is just a mess without a clue

Of all the best that can come true

If you know What and Which and Who.

Respond to Pooh by putting together a Mission Statement, a paragraph that summarizes your goals in life.

Suggested Projects: *Finding Happiness, Winning the Lottery, Grappling with Groups.*

Chapter 9

COMMUNICATION

Most people don't realize the magnitude of that endeavor. We had millions of people working on thousands of projects around the world in the 1960's. We knew good communication would be required to achieve our goal; therefore, we designed the simplest – yet most effective – communication system possible, and that was the key to our success.

---A space engineer on the moon landing project

A study of married couples was conducted in which each spouse was wired with a microphone for a week. The total amount of time the couple spent in conversation with each other was extracted from the recording tapes, including any and all words directed from one partner to the other. One could argue that the microphones were somewhat inhibiting – the amount of shouting would certainly not increase, would it? Taking such considerations into account, how long do you think the average couple spent in communicating for the week? (Answer at the end of chapter).

The problem of communication is so important, so pervasive, that we have given it a whole chapter of its own. Here we will collect material that addresses this problem, especially as it relates to the rest of the book. What is communication? We can think of it as the process of conveying understanding from one person or group to another. By using

 the word "understanding," we emphasize the most difficult aspect of communication. It is easy to convey words or gestures or tone of voice, these are the tools of communication. But to convey true understanding presents a real problem. Fortunately, we can apply PSSSP techniques to this as to any other problem.

- We can be **P**roactive by developing in our own minds a clear idea of the concept or feeling that we want to convey.

- We can **S**ee it more clearly by pondering all the possible barriers to communication.

- We can **S**implify the problem by choosing the right words and actions to convey the concept.

- We can **S**tir it up by practicing what we have to say or write, and by soliciting feedback during the communication process.

- We can **P**ause and Reflect at every opportunity, to monitor communication progress and weigh possible alternatives.

Of course, in every communication process there are senders and receivers. The strategies we have just listed are sending strategies. Try **P**ausing and Reflecting at this point in order to write up a list of PSSSP strategies for the receiver in a communications process.

Discuss the following list of ideas for improving communication. They were presented at a middle school workshop on parent-child communication. Do the ideas fall under any of the PSSSP headings?

- Timing

- Humor

- Seek solutions

- Be open-minded

- No instant judgement – check it out

- Open body language

- Attentiveness

- Avoid interrupting

- Respect and honesty

Groups rather than individuals solve most real-world problems. Many experts on learning feel that group work can be an important component of the classroom experience. For example, collaborative group work promotes active learning, fosters a sense of community in the classroom, creates a classroom culture in which students feel comfortable discussing and debating mathematical ideas, and prepares students to function in the real world.

Team Performance Agreement

We have noted that it makes sense to use a group approach in an academic setting. A group has the potential to achieve results far beyond the capability of any one member. What is the best way to accomplish effective team performance? The most fundamental requirement is for every member of the team to have a common vision of team goals and expectations. One way to establish this vision is to develop **a Team Performance Agreement** (TPA). The TPA can provide a framework for group efforts, outlining what is expected of each member, how decisions will be made and how conflicts will be resolved. As you prepare a TPA, keep in mind that project reports will be graded on accuracy, presentation and creativity. Specific items that should be addressed in the TPA include the following:

1. What does the group consider an acceptable performance level? The bare minimum? The top mark on each assignment? Should every member obtain working knowledge of all the concepts involved in the project?

2. How are decisions to be made, especially when no consensus can be reached? Do team members accept the will of the majority? The most effective agreements emphasize the importance of understanding all views in a dispute and seeking an alternative that is acceptable to all parties.

3. How will roles be identified for individual members? How will the group deal with inferior performance by team members (failure to show at meetings, contribute to

project solutions, etc.)? Each individual brings unique talents to the group, talents that should be encouraged.

4. How will effective communication be promoted within the group? How will the group insure that all members contribute ideas? That all members listen carefully to others?

A carefully prepared TPA can avert an exponentially increasing number of team problems and lead to satisfying and enjoyable cooperation. Before you finalize your TPA, you might want to ponder the following problem, based on actual classroom events. Good luck.

Grappling With Groups.

Andy, Barb, Carl, and Dawn had been put together for group problem solving in their math class. They introduced themselves and Barb wrote down the name and phone number of each group member. Their first job was to put together a Team Performance Agreement. They went through the guidelines the teacher had provided, with Carl suggesting responses to each point and Barb writing them down. Once in a while Dawn or Andy would add a comment. They agreed that "disagreements would be handled by a discussion and a majority decision" and that "team members not participating in an assignment would receive reduced credit." By the end of the class they had a rough draft of a TPA and Carl suggested that Andy type it up. The finished assignment was due the next class period (Monday) and they agreed that Andy would bring the typed copy to class for everyone to sign. On Monday, however, Andy didn't show up in class. Frantic calls to his room found only an answering machine. Barb, Carl and Dawn were upset, but had no choice other than to type up the report (Dawn did it) and turn it in late on Wednesday. Andy came to class on Wednesday claiming that he had tried to call Barb on Sunday night, but kept getting busy signals. He couldn't remember Carl's or Dawn's last name, and therefore couldn't call them. He had learned he would be unable to attend class on Monday and wanted to notify his other group members. When he wasn't able to contact anyone, he "assumed they didn't need him" and came to class on Wednesday ready to sign the TPA along with everyone else. Dawn was furious and wanted to exclude him from the assignment. Barb and Carl were also angry, but weren't sure how to handle the "team" situation. They asked the teacher to resolve the conflict.

1. Should the teacher provide a resolution? If so, in what way?

2. If not, how do you think the team should resolve the situation?

3. In what ways could the problem have been avoided?

4. What could the group do to avoid or handle similar problems in the future?

Writing as Communication

Writing is an essential form of communication. Here is a checklist that should be followed when preparing written problem solutions.

Does this paper:

1. Clearly (re)state the problem to be solved?

2. Provide a paragraph that explains how the problem will be approached?

3. State the answer in a few complete sentences that stand on their own?

4. Give a precise and well-organized explanation of how the answer was found?

5. Clearly label diagrams, tables, graphs, or other visual representations?

6. Define all variables, terminology, and notation used?

7. Clearly state the assumptions that underlie the formulas and other results, and explain how each is derived or provide a reference?

8. Give acknowledgment where it is due?

9. Use correct spelling, grammar, and punctuation?

10. Contain correct mathematics?

11. Solve the problems that were originally asked?

(Adapted from Tommy Ratlliff, Wheaton College)

Suggested Projects: *Finding Happiness, Grappling With Groups.*

Answer to question at the start of the chapter: The average couple conversed for a total of 17 minutes during the week.

Chapter 10

STRETCHES

This chapter contains shorter problems, designed to stretch your mental muscles.

1. What are the next two letters in the following sequence? OTTFFSSE.

2. Move just one line and leave the giraffe unchanged (it can be oriented differently).

3. In a village of 800 women, 3% wear one earring. Of the remaining 97%, half wear two earrings and half wear none. How many earrings are worn?

4. A piece of string is 10 inches long. How many scissor cuts are needed to get 10 one-inch pieces?

5. Use three 7's and mathematical symbols to construct an expression equal to 20.

6. Five circles balance six triangles. One square balances a circle and triangle together. How many squares balance eleven triangles?

7. Put 8 playing cards in the squares so that two Aces touch Kings, two Kings touch

Queens, two Queens touch Jacks, two Jacks can touch anybody.

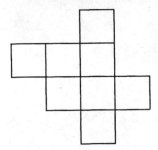

8. How many flags could you plant on the surface of the earth (including oceans) so that the distance between any two flags is the same?

9. Place two coins of the same size flat on a table and roll one around the edge of the other, as if they were gears. When the rolling coin has made one trip around the circumference of the fixed coin, how many times will it have revolved around its own center? What if the coins are different sizes? What if the fixed one is a square?

10. You just saved a kingdom from a dragon and the queen offers you a reward from her collection of solid golden spheres. She says that you can take either two golden spheres, each of whose diameters is the length of her royal index finger; or a single golden sphere whose diameter is twice the length of her index finger. Which do you choose?

11. Nine dots are placed in a square array, three rows of three. Without lifting your pencil from the paper, draw four straight lines that pass through all the dots. Can you do it with fewer lines?

12. If you cut a pizza into 45-degree wedges meeting at a point other than the center and two people eat alternate slices, do they each get the same amount?

13. An examination in three subjects, Algebra, Biology and Chemistry, was taken by 41 students. The following table shows how many students failed in each single subject and in their various combinations.

Subjects	A	B	C	AB	AC	BC	ABC
Failed	12	5	8	2	6	3	1

How many students passed all three subjects?

14. Three toothpicks can be used to form a triangle. How many triangles can be formed with six toothpicks?

15. Land in Problemia costs $100 per square foot. What is the most you could pay for a triangular piece of land that measures 75 feet by 50 feet by 25 feet?

16. What is the sum of the first 1000 odd positive integers?

17. Which is bigger, 100000001/100000002 or 200000001/200000002?

18. What is the largest number of pizza pieces you can have after making 10 straight cuts in a pizza?

19. A game is played with 30 chips, each with a red face and a green face. The chips are arranged in a circle, showing a random pattern of red and green faces. A move consists of taking away a green disk and flipping over its neighbors. The resulting gap is not closed up, so the remaining disks do not acquire new neighbors. The goal is to remove all the disks. For which patterns of red and green is this possible?

20. You have eight cubes that look the same, but one is slightly heavier than the others. How many weighings on a balance are required to determine the heavy cube?

21. Find the sum of the integers from 1 to 300 that are multiples of neither 3 nor 4.

22. What is the rightmost nonzero digit in the product $1 \cdot 2 \cdot 3 \cdot 4 \cdot \ldots \cdot 100$?

23. There are 25 people at a party. Each person has a certain number of friends at the party, not including herself. If A is friends with B, then B is friends with A. Must there be two partygoers with the same number of friends?

24. How many times a day do the digits on a digital clock add to 22? At what times?

25. Solve this cryptarithmetic problem. EGG + EGG = PAGE

26. Assign True or False to each sentence.

F 1. Sentence 5 is false.

T 2. Sentence 1 is false.

T 3. Sentence 4 is true.

T 4. Only one of these sentences is false.

T 5. Sentences 2 and 3 are both true or both false.

27. Make a magic square. Put the digits from 1 to 9 in a 3 by 3 array so that all rows, all columns and both diagonals give the same sum.

28. Merlin the Magician encountered three individuals on the road. Though he didn't know them, he knew one was a knight. He also knew that spies always lied, knights always told the truth and peasants sometimes lied and sometimes told the truth. The three spoke as follows:

A: B is a spy

B: A is a knight

C: Either A or B is telling the truth.

Who was the knight? Could Merlin determine what the others were?

29. I will play a game called *Fifteen* with you. We take turns placing coins on the squares

in the strip:

1	2	3	4	5	6	7	8	9

I place quarters and you place nickels. The first one to cover precisely three different

numbers that add to 15 wins all the money. Why am I willing to bet more than you?

30. When the farm burned, they found a bill: 72 turkeys, $_67.9_. The fire smudge

obliterated the first and last digit of the total price of the birds. What are the two faded

digits and what was the price of a single turkey?

31. There were three women in bathing suits. One was crying, but she was happy. The

other two were smiling, but they were sad. What was going on?

32. Estimate the length of the front wall, the area of the ceiling and the volume of the

room.

33. Why are manhole covers round?

34. Estimate the undergraduate enrollment at the main campus of your university. Give

an interval in which you are 90% certain the answer lies (for example, 15,000 to 15,250).

35. A pilot flies south 100 miles, then east 100 miles, then north 100 miles and ends up back where she started. Where might she have started?

36. You have a 5-quart and an 8-quart container and an unlimited supply of water. How do you measure precisely 7 quarts?

37. Amy wants a piece of land, exactly level, which has four boundary lines. Two boundary lines run exactly north-south, the two others exactly east-west, and each boundary line is 100 yards. Can Amy buy such a piece of land in the U.S.?

38. You have just entered the cave of wonders, where you find 7 identical looking spheres. A wizard has told you that (1) each sphere is colored on the inside; (2) one of the colors occurs for a strict majority of the spheres (4 or more); (3) when two spheres of the same color touch each other, they both glow in color. Using as few comparisons as possible, find a single sphere that has the majority color. How many comparisons do you need?

39. A worm is at the bottom of a forty-meter hole. It can crawl upward four meters during daylight, but at night it slips back three meters. At this rate, how long will it take the worm to crawl out of the hole?

40. Add one line to IX to get an expression equal to 6.

41. The rock group U2 has a concert that starts in 17 minutes and they must all cross a bridge to get there. All four begin on the same side of the bridge. It is night and there is only one flashlight. A maximum of two people can cross at one time. Any group that crosses must carry the flashlight. The flashlight must be walked back and forth, it cannot be thrown, for example. Each band member walks at a different speed and a pair must walk at the slower member's speed. The speeds are:

Bono: 1 minute to cross

Edge: 2 minutes to cross

Adam: 5 minutes to cross

Larry: 10 minutes to cross.

Can you help them to get to the concert on time?

42. Place numbers in the blanks so that the following sentence is true: "In this sentence, the number of occurrences of 0 is _, of 1 is _, of 2 is _, of 3 is _, of 4 is _, of 5 is _, of 6 is _, of 7 is _, of 8 is _, and of 9 is _."

43. There are three light switches on the wall at the end of a hall. At the other end of the hall is a room with a closed door. Inside the room is a lamp on a table. One of the switches controls the lamp. If you are allowed exactly one trip into the room (leaving the door closed behind you), how do you determine which switch controls the lamp?

44. Divide a sheet of paper into eight parts. Number them on one side as shown in the diagram. Fold the paper along the lines to form a packet (like a folded map) with number

1 face-up on top, followed by the other numbers in order.

7	4	3	2
6	5	8	1

45. I have some little cubes. I can arrange them into four squares each of a different size. I can also arrange them into three squares, each of a different size. How many cubes do I need?

46. How many minutes is it before 6 o'clock if 50 minutes ago it was four times as many minutes past 3 o'clock?

47. Do, Re and Mi have ages that sum to 33. Mi is two years older than Re. When Re is Mi's present age, Do will be Re's present age. What are their ages?

48. Are there more perfect squares between 2 and 1000 than between 1000 and 4000?

49. The year 1996 was a special year for my grandfather, the student said. In that year his age was equal to the product of the four digits of his birth year. The same was true for my mother. In what years were they born?

50. "The farmer owns at least 100 acres," said Mo. "Fewer than 100 acres," said Larry. "He owns at least one acre," said Curly. If exactly one of them is telling the truth, who is it?

51. Eight Intergalactic Starships from different galaxies each aim their single Killer Phasor beams at an enemy ship and fire. How many survivors are there?

52. A certain crystal grows in rectangular prisms whose length, width, and depth (measured in units of molecular spacing) are necessarily three consecutive whole numbers (e.g. $L = 25$, $W = 26$, $D = 27$). Prove that the number of molecules in any such crystal is an exact multiple of 6.

53. Ten people are sitting around a round table. The sum of ten dollars is to be distributed among them according to the rule that each person receives one half of the sum that his two neighbors receive jointly. Is there a way to distribute the money?

54. Bob's stamp collection consists of three books. Two tenths of his stamps are in the first book, several sevenths in the second book, and there are 303 stamps in the third book. How many stamps has Bob?

55. How old is the captain, how many children has he and how long is his boat? The product of the three desired numbers (integers) is 32118. The length of the boat is in feet (is several feet), the captain has both sons and daughters, he has more years than children, but he is not yet one hundred years old.

56. It was a hot day and the 4 couples drank 44 glasses of iced tea. Ann had 2, Betty 3, Carol 4 and Lisa 5 glasses. Mr. Brown drank just as many glasses as his wife, but each of the other men drank more than his wife: Mr. Green twice, Mr. White three times and Mr. Smith four times as many glasses. What are the last names of the four ladies?

57. "How many children have you and how old are they?" asked the mathematics teacher.

"I have three boys," said Mrs. Smith. "The product of their ages is 72 and the sum of their ages is the street number on this building."

The teacher went to look at the entrance, came back and said: "That doesn't tell me the answer."

"True," said Mrs. Smith, "but I still hope that the oldest boy will some day be a mathematician."

What are the ages of the boys?

58. Six glasses are placed in a row. The first three are filled with juice, the second three are empty. By moving only one glass, can you arrange them so that empty and full glasses alternate?

59. You throw away the outside and cook the inside. Then you eat the outside and throw away the inside. What did you eat?

60. Why are 1998 American dollar bills worth more than 1997 American dollar bills?

61. Rearrange the letters in the words *new door* to make one word.

62. Put ten horses in 9 stalls.

63. Three cannibals and three missionaries must cross a river. They have only one boat that holds only two people. Complicating matters is the fact that if cannibals outnumber missionaries in a group, then the cannibals eat the missionaries. How do they all cross safely?

64. There are four cards, with a letter on one side and a number on the other side, lying on a table.

$$\boxed{E} \quad \boxed{F} \quad \boxed{4} \quad \boxed{5}$$

Which cards *must* you turn over to verify the following statement:

"All cards with a vowel on one side have an even number on the other."

65. A cube of wood 3 inches on each edge is to be cut into cubes 1 inch on an edge. After each cut with a (very thin) saw, the pieces may be piled in any manner you wish before the next cut. What is the smallest number of cuts required?

66. Move three matchsticks to make the fish swim in the opposite direction:

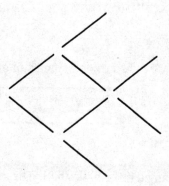

67. Estimate the number of (whole) pizzas this class eats in a year.

68. Move two of the toothpicks that make up the sides of the squares to create exactly four squares.

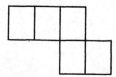

69. Estimate the number of hairs on your head. Determine a 90% confidence interval for the answer.

70. Use precisely the four digits 1,3,4,6 (no repeats) and the four arithmetic operations (in any combination) to make an expression equal to 24.

71. Arrange 5 quarters so they all touch each other. Arrange 6 cigarettes so they all touch each other. Can you do it with 7 cigarettes?

72. Move two matchsticks so that the olive is outside the martini glass:

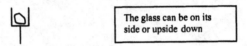

The glass can be on its
side or upside down

73. A string is wrapped around the diameter of a basketball. The string is then lengthened by 5 feet and made into a circle with the basketball at the middle. Now imagine a string wrapped around the earth, lengthened by 5 feet and reformed into a circle with the earth in the center. Is the string farther away from the basketball or from the earth?

Chapter 11

PROJECTS

Teachers open the door .... you enter by yourself.

---Chinese Proverb

In this chapter we present a list of more open-ended problems on which you can hone your **PP**roblem **SSS**olving skills. The problems can be solved individually or as group projects over an extended period.

Acrobats. You are the manager of a troupe of acrobats. Each wears a different outfit, consisting of a top and tights. Both the tops and tights come in blue, red and yellow. How many acrobats are in the troupe? The king wants to hire a royal team of acrobats from your troupe - three acrobats wearing tops that are all the same or all different colors, and tights that are all the same or all different. He agrees to let you send one acrobat at a time to the throne room, where they accumulate until he can select a royal team from the acrobats gathered there. If he pays you $100 for each acrobat you send over, how much money can you make?

Body Cells. How many cells might be found in an averaged-sized adult human body? What is a reasonable lower estimate? Upper estimate?

Bouncing Bishop. A Bishop moves any number of squares along the diagonals on a chessboard. In other words, it moves in a straight line along squares of the same color, which we call "his color." In this problem we will put the Bishop at the corner of a rectangular chessboard and move him in a straight line until he comes to an edge. Then he will "bounce" off the edge (angle of incidence equals angle of reflection) and continue in a straight line until he bounces off another edge. If the chessboard is square, then the Bishop will bounce back and forth along one diagonal (See it). On the other hand, if the chessboard has four rows and 6 columns, the Bishop will eventually pass across all the squares of his color.

The problem is to decide what size chessboards will permit the Bishop to pass across all the squares of his color.

Chair Challenge. A square chair has a leg at each corner. The chair is so heavy that it can only be moved by rotating it 90 degrees on one leg. Can you move the chair one chair-width to the right so that it faces in the same direction?

start   finish

If the chair is twice as wide as it is long, can you move it one (double) width to the right?

Checkerboard Chase. Player A begins by placing a checker on the lower left-hand corner of a checkerboard (8 by 8 squares). Player B places a checker one square to the right or one square up or one square diagonally up and to the right of Player A's checker. Then A places a checker one square to the right or one square up or one square diagonally up and to the right of Player B. The players continue alternating moves in this way. The winner is the player who places a checker in the upper right corner. Would you rather be Player A or Player B?

Circle Dance. At the High School Junior Prom, seven students got up from their seats in order to dance their favorite circle dance. As the students arrived at the dance area, the process of "lining up" became complicated due to past dating histories. They realized that even casual contact between some of them might result in an ugly scene and would not be a good idea. The chart below indicates which pairs of students have friendly relations (F) and can stand next to each other during the dance. The other pairs are not friends (NF) and cannot stand next to each other. Find all the ways in which the students can line up for the circle dance.

	Aaron	Ben	Carl	Denise	Elsa	Faye	Gail
Aaron		F	NF	NF	F	NF	NF
Ben	F		F	F	NF	NF	F
Carl	NF	F		NF	F	F	F
Denise	NF	F	NF		F	F	NF
Elsa	F	NF	F	F		F	F
Faye	NF	NF	F	F	F		NF
Gail	NF	f	F	NF	F	NF	

Commuter. A commuter rides the train to and from work each day. Her husband meets her at the train station and drives her home. One day the commuter leaves work early, catches a different train and arrives at the station one hour ahead of schedule. It being a nice day, she decides to walk toward home. Somewhere along the way she meets her husband, driving from home to pick her up at the usual time. She gets in the car and they drive back, arriving 20 minutes earlier than normal. How long was the commuter walking?

Cryptarithmetic Problems (Sachar [26])

1.

```
      S   H   E
  +   E   E   L
  _____
  E   L   S   E
```

2.

```
  S   T   A   Y   S
  +       S   A   Y
  _____
  T   R   U   S   T
```

3.

```
      S   E   E   D
  +   I   C   E   D
  _____
  S   P   I   C   E
```

4. Why is this problem impossible?

```
      F   O   U   R
  +   E   I   G   H   T
  _____
  T   W   E   L   V   E
```

112

5.

```
         R   Y   E
  ×          B   E
  ─────────────────
         A   R   E
  E   A   T
  ─────────────────
  W   E   R   E
```

6.

```
         S   T   R   A   W
  ×                   T   O
  ────────────────────────
         W   A   R   T   S
     S   T   R   A   W
  ────────────────────────
     C   H   A   I   R   S
```

7. $\dfrac{EVE}{DID}$ = .TALKTALKTALK..... (The fraction EVE/DID has been reduced to lowest

terms) (Stir)

Cycling Heaps. Starting with a collection of several heaps of beans, we create a new collection of heaps by removing one bean from each original heap to make a new heap. Each original heap shrinks by one. For example, if we start with four heaps of 1,1,2,5 beans, we end up with three heaps of 1,4,4 beans after one "move". It doesn't matter in what order the heaps are listed. Here are some questions about this process.

1. When is the new collection of heaps the SAME as the original collection of heaps after one move? Does this ever happen?

2. What happens when you continue creating new collections of heaps by repeating the process described above? Does the sequence of collections start repeating no matter what collection you start with?

3. Can you design a collection of heaps so that you can repeat the "new collection" process 5 times without getting two collections the same? How about 10 times? How about "n" times?

Dating Service. A dating service has as clients 6 recently divorced couples. Each client wants the opportunity to socialize with the other clients of the opposite sex, but refuses to be in the same room as his or her ex-spouse. The service wants to throw a sequence of parties to bring people together. They want each male and female pair to attend some party (not necessarily as a couple), but of course no formerly married couple should attend the same party. Is it possible to do this? If so, what is the fewest number of parties that can be held? What are all the possible sequences that have the fewest number of parties?

Desert Delivery. Here you are at a desert oasis with 600 liters of gasoline that is sorely needed at an outpost 1000 kilometers away. Your small jeep can only carry 200 liters at a time, and burns one liter for every 5 kilometers it travels. How many liters of gasoline can you deliver safely to the outpost?

Different Angle. What is the angle made by the two line segments shown on the cube, passing between the midpoints of the edges?

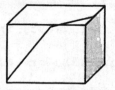

Die Hard III. You have a 4-quart container and a 9-quart container and an unlimited supply of water. How do you measure *exactly* 6 quarts?

Dollar Auction. (Taylor [36]) The dollar auction is an elementary model of escalatory behavior such as the buildup of American troops in Viet Nam or the arms race of the 1960's, 70's and 80's. It is an excellent vehicle to introduce the mathematical analysis of decision trees. In a dollar auction, two players bid for a STAKE held by an auctioneer. We will use an example in which the stake is $3. Each player has a BANKROLL. In our example each player has a bankroll of $3. The players bid in turn (in whole dollars) until there is a pass. At this point the highest bidder pays her last bid to the auctioneer and receives the stake. The catch is that the other player must pay his last bid to the auctioneer as well. The problem is to determine the best bidding strategy for each player.

Note: To simplify matters, we assume that both players follow the *Conservative Convention*—If either bidder determines that two or more different bids will lead to the same eventual outcome for herself, and that no bids will lead to a better outcome, then the bidder will choose the smallest of those bids (that is, the conservative bid). To illustrate the Conservative Convention, suppose that in our example above, Player 1 bids $2. Now Player 2 can only bid $3. But this will result in a net gain of $0 to Player 2, the same outcome as Passing (bidding $0). Under the Conservative Convention, Player 2 passes, so Player 1 pays the auctioneer $2 and receives the stake of $3, a net gain of $1. Note that if Player 2 had bid $3, then Player 1 would lose $2. This is not allowed under the Conservative Convention. In particular, punishing the other player is not a goal of the game (although it is a goal in military build-up situations).

By the way, we also assume that each player has full knowledge of the other player's strategy, including the fact that the other player will use the Conservative Convention. So I know you will use the Conservative Convention, that you know I know that, that you know I know that you know I know that and so on. And again, making the other player lose money is not a goal.

1. Determine the best bidding strategies if the STAKE is 3 and each player has BANKROLL 3.

2. Determine the best bidding strategy if the STAKE is 4 and each player has BANKROLL 3.

3. Experiment with other stakes and bankrolls to see if you can come up with a general rule.

You don't need to assume that both players have the same bankroll. Your rule should show that if the stake is 20 and the bankroll is 100 for each player, then the best opening bid is 5.

Dominoes. How many ways can you cover a 2 by 10 rectangle with dominoes (2 by 1 rectangles)?

Dominoes Again. A domino is rectangle divided into two squares, with between 0 and 6 dots placed in each square. Instead of dots we will use a digit between 0 and 6. Two dominoes can be placed end-to-end when the squares at which the dominoes meet are labeled with the same digits (digits can be upside down). Suppose you are given dominoes with the following labelings: [1,2], [1,4], [1,6], [2,3], [2,6], [3,5], [3,4], [4,5], [5,6]. Can you arrange them all in a row in accordance with the matching digit rule so that the first number in the row is the same as the last number in the row? If not, what extra dominoes do you need?

Factorials. How many zeros appear at the end of 100! (Note: 100! = (100)(99)(98)••••(1), the product of the integers from 1 to 100.)

Faculty Debts. The accountant complains to the mathematician: "I lent money to five faculty members and still haven't been paid back. You are one of them; the other four owe me 12 dollars altogether, but I don't remember how much each person owes me separately."

"Are the debts in whole dollars?"

"Yes. I do remember that the four other debts multiplied together equals your debt. Do you remember how much you owe me?"

"Yes, but I still haven't figured out how much each of the other four owe you."

"Wait! The statistician is the one who owes the least."

"That does it. Now I know the amount of each debt."

If you were the mathematician, could you determine the amounts?

Finding Happiness. Explain how the ideas of PSSSP could be applied to the problem of finding happiness in life. Include specific examples from your own experience.

Forty Thieves. Forty thieves, all of different ages, steal a huge pile of identical gold coins and must decide how to divide them up. They settle on the following procedure. The youngest divides the coins among the thieves however he wishes, then all 40 thieves vote on whether they are satisfied with the division. If at least half vote YES, the division is accepted. If a majority votes NO, the youngest is killed and the next youngest gets to try to divide the loot among the remaining 39 thieves (including herself). Again they all vote, with the same penalty if the majority votes NO. And so on. Each of the thieves is logical and always acts in her or his own self-interest, ignoring the interest of the group, fairness, etc. Given all this, how should the youngest of the 40 thieves divide the loot?

Four Bean Heaps. There are four heaps of beans on the table with 3,4,5, and 6 beans, respectively. You and a partner alternate moves until the beans are gone, and the player removing the last bean(s) wins. A move consists of either of the following:

(i) Removing a single bean from a heap as long as at least two beans remain in that heap.

(ii) Removing a complete heap of 2 or 3 beans.

What is a winning strategy?

Fuses. You have two fuses, each 12'' long. Each fuse burns in exactly one hour, but does not necessarily burn at a uniform rate. Also, the two fuses do not necessarily burn at the same rate over corresponding segments. But a given segment on a given fuse burns in the same amount of time in either direction. How do you use these two fuses to time 15 minutes? Extra credit - how do you time 15 minutes using only one fuse?

Graphs. Given any graph is it possible to color the vertices black and white in such a way that at least half the neighbors of every white vertex are black and at least half the neighbors of every black vertex are white?

Grandfather. In 1996 my grandfather's age equaled the product of the four digits in the year he was born and the same was true for his daughter. Find the two birth years.

Grappling with Groups. Andy, Barb, Carl, and Dawn had been put together for group problem solving in their math class. They introduced themselves and Barb wrote down the name and phone number of each group member. Their first job was to put together a Team Performance Agreement. They went down the list the teacher had provided, with Carl suggesting responses to each point and Barb writing them down. Once in a while Dawn or Andy would add a comment. They agreed that "disagreements would be handled by a discussion and a majority decision" and that "team members not participating in an assignment would receive reduced credit." By the end of the class they had a rough draft of a TPA and Carl suggested that Andy type it up. The finished assignment was due the next class period (Monday) and they agreed that Andy would bring the typed copy to class for everyone to sign. On Monday, however, Andy didn't show up in class. Frantic calls to his room found only an answering machine. Barb, Carl and Dawn were upset, but had no choice other than to type up the report (Dawn did it) and turn it in late on Wednesday. Andy came to class on Wednesday claiming that he had tried to call Barb on Sunday night, but kept getting busy signals. He couldn't remember Carl's or Dawn's last name, and therefore couldn't call them. He had learned he would be unable to attend class on Monday and wanted to notify his other group members. When he wasn't able to contact anyone, he "assumed they didn't need him" and came to class on Wednesday ready to sign the TPA along with everyone else. Dawn was furious and wanted to exclude him from the assignment. Barb and Carl were also angry, but weren't sure how to handle the "team" situation. They asked the teacher to resolve the conflict.

1. Should the teacher provide a resolution? If so, in what way?

2. If not, how do you think the team should resolve the situation?

3. In what ways could the problem have been avoided?

4. What could the group do to avoid or handle similar problems in the future?

Grilled Cheese. You need to make five grilled cheese sandwiches. You have a grill that is large enough to toast two sandwiches at a time. The sandwiches must be toasted one minute on each side. It takes 3 seconds to flip a sandwich and 5 seconds to take one off or put one on the grill. What is the shortest amount of time needed to toast all five sandwiches ?

Handshakes. In a train station waiting room you find yourself waiting for the train along with 15 other travelers. Everyone in the room decides that it is a good idea to become acquainted by shaking hands with everyone else in the room. How many handshakes will take place?

Heap of Beans. You and a friend are playing a game with a pile of 16 beans. You alternate turns and on each turn you must remove 1,2 or 3 beans from the heap. The player to remove the last bean(s) from the pile wins. Should you go first or second? Describe a winning strategy.

House Hunt. (Personal Communication, Doug Tinney) There are five houses in a row. Each house has one pet, one color, one resident, one drink and one vehicle.

- Tim lives in the red house

- Lon owns a pet dog

- Coffee is drunk in the green house

- Hal drinks water

- The green house is immediately to the right of the ivory house

- The truck driver owns pet snails

- A bike is parked in front of the yellow house

- Tea is drunk in the middle house

- Vic lives in the first house

- The Cadillac driver lives next to the man with the pet fox

- The house with the bike is next to the house with a pet horse

- The Ford driver drinks Pepsi

- Winnie drives an MGB

- Vic lives next door to the blue house.

Who drinks the vodka? Who owns the pet worms?

Inequality. If A,B,C,D are numbers between 0 and 1, show that

$$(1-A)(1-B)(1-C)(1-D) > 1 - A - B - C - D.$$

Interview. Pick someone you know and admire who frequently solves problems in her work. Interview your choice about what kinds of problems she solves and what techniques she finds helpful in solving those problems. Then integrate the answers you get into the PSSSP framework to whatever extent you can. Fully explain why you can or cannot use the PSSSP headings. Your report will be based on accuracy, creativity and presentation.

Judge. You are a judge and two suspects are brought before you. One is a murderer and the other is not. One always lies and the other always tells the truth. What question can you ask one of the suspects to determine who is the murderer?

Largest Lake. The Fish and Wildlife service is conducting a Purple Loosestrife eradication experiment. Purple Loosestrife is a beautiful but destructive plant that has invaded many of the wetlands in New England after having been planted in Massachusetts by a well-meaning botanist. The scientist working on the project has a choice of two lakes for conducting the experiment and would like to choose the lake with smaller surface area so that there will be less damage if something goes wrong. Aerial views of the two lakes are reproduced below on the same scale (1 inch = 100 feet). Can you help Fish and Wildlife decide which is smaller?

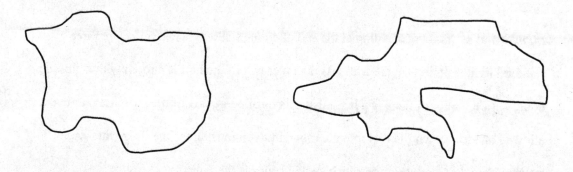

Laser Treatment. As a medical doctor you are treating a patient afflicted with a malignant tumor in his stomach. If you do not remove the tumor, the patient will die. You have, at your disposal, a laser ray that will destroy the tumor. Unfortunately, the intensity of the ray required to destroy the tumor will also destroy all healthy tissue in its path. If you lowered the intensity of the ray to a certain level, you could shoot it into the body without harming any healthy tissue. This lower intensity, however, would not eliminate the tumor. Can you save the patient?

After you have discussed your ideas on this problem, read the following story.

A Story: A general wanted to attack a fortress in the center of a town. The enemy, however, had mined all of the roads leading to the fortress. If the general marched the army over the roads, the vibrations would set off the mines and destroy the army. Craftily, the general split the army into small squads, dispersed them along the roads leading to the fortress so that they all arrived simultaneously at the fortress and, together, defeated the enemy. Any new thoughts? Do you need the following?

Lease or Buy. Is it better to lease a new car or buy it?

Light Switches. You are standing at the end of a long hallway where there are three standard light switches on the wall. At the other end of the hall is a room with a closed door. Inside the room there is a lamp that is controlled by one of the switches. You are allowed one trip down the hall into the room, but you must close the door when you return. How do you determine which switch controls the lamp?

Magic Cuts. Cut the table in three pieces, along the lines to get equal totals on each piece. One cut is shown at the right. Can you find another, and possibly even a third?

2	5	6
9	1	8
4	3	7

2	5	6
9	1	8
4	3	7

Maple Tree. Determine the height of a tall maple tree located somewhere at your. Use at least two different methods.

Milk and Coffee. An 8-ounce cup of coffee and an 8-ounce cup of milk are sitting side by side. You take a tablespoon of milk and stir it into the coffee. Then you take a tablespoon of the mix and stir it back in the milk. Is there more milk in the coffee or coffee in the milk?

Try this experiment to help you think about the problem. Make 10 pieces of black paper to represent the coffee and 10 pieces of white paper to represent the milk. Pretend a tablespoon is three pieces of paper. Put a tablespoon (3 white pieces) of milk into the coffee. Then put a tablespoon of the mix (three pieces – how many possibilities?) back into the milk. Do you end up with more white pieces in the black or more black pieces in the white? Record your results carefully.

Multiple Locks. You belong to a Math Club that has accumulated valuable jewelry (gold pens, platinum protractors, etc.). The treasure is kept in a chest. For security reasons, you want at least two of your 10 club members present when the chest is open. To insure this, you put multiple locks on the chest and distribute keys to members so that no one member can open the chest, but any two members can. Each lock has a different key, but you can make several copies of the same key to distribute to the club members. What is the fewest number of locks and keys that you will need?

Neighbor Knockout. Five Imperial Storm Troopers stand in a circle, draw their blasters and vaporize either the neighbor to the immediate left or the neighbor to the immediate right. The vaporizers are short range, and can't touch the two people in the circle who are not nearest neighbors. It is possible for neighbors to vaporize each other. If any two adjacent Storm Troopers remain, then they play a second round, vaporizing a neighbor of choice. How many survivors are there? What if there are more than five storm troopers?

What if they don't stand in a circle, but can still only vaporize nearest neighbors? Have you seen other problems like this?

Nim. Make three rows of pennies with 3 pennies in the first row, 5 in the second and 7 in the third. Two players alternate removing pennies from a row. You can remove any number of pennies, but only from a single row. The player to remove the last penny or pennies wins. What is a winning strategy?

Ordinal Games. (Taylor [36]) Very simple two-player games can provide insight into complicated and important historical events. For this project we will study 2 by 2 ordinal games. In this type of game the two players are called Row and Column. Each player has two options, to Cooperate or Not. A choice of an option is called a strategy. A play of the game occurs when Row and Column simultaneously choose an option (C or N). An outcome of the game is a pair of options. For example, NC signifies that Row chose N and Column chose C. Each player ranks the four possible outcomes (why 4?) with the values 4,3,2,1, with 4 being the worst rank and 1 the best. Here is a matrix representation of a possible ranking scheme.

	C	N
C	(3,3)	(1,4)
N	(4,1)	(2,2)

The first number of the pairs indicates Row's ranking of the corresponding outcome, the second number is Column's ranking. For example, Column ranked the outcome NC as best (1).

- How many different ways could you put number pairs into this game matrix?

- In the matrix above, strategy C is a dominant strategy for Row. That is, no matter what column chooses, it is best for Row to choose C. Does Column have a dominant strategy?

Note: The outcome CC in the matrix is called a Nash equilibrium point (after John Nash who won the 1996 Nobel Prize in Economics). Neither player gains by unilaterally changing strategy.

(A) *Chicken*, two cars roar at each other down the middle of a deserted country road. Each driver has two options: Swerve or Not Swerve. Call the drivers Row and Column and rank the possible outcomes for each, explaining your rankings. Use the rankings to produce a game matrix like the one above. Identify any dominant strategies and Nash equilibrium points.

(B) *Prisoner's Dilemma*, two suspects have been arrested and charged with jointly stealing a milking machine. They are separated and, having been read their rights, are given a choice of remaining Silent or Confessing. The outcomes result in different penalties. If both remain silent, they will each receive a one-year sentence based on a sure conviction on lesser charges. If both confess, they will each receive a five-year sentence. If one confesses and one remains silent, the confessor will go free as state's evidence, while the silent one gets a ten-year prison term based on the confession of his partner. produce a game matrix for Prisoner's Dilemma and discuss dominant strategies and Nash equilibrium points.

(C) *Gambling with God.* There are two boxes labeled A and B. You have a choice between taking box B alone or taking both A and B. God has placed $1000 in box A. In box B, God placed $1,000,000 if God knew you would choose box B. Box B contains nothing if God knew you would choose both boxes. What should you do? Hundreds of philosophical papers have been written on this problem. Most people think the answer is obvious, but split about evenly on which choice is correct.

Give an argument that says you should choose box B alone.

Give an argument that says you should take both boxes.

Which argument do you find more compelling?

Make up a 2 by 2 ordinal game to model this problem. You may fiddle with the rules.

Parking Lot. You pull into the mall on a Saturday shopping trip only to find all the spaces full. Instead of driving around looking for a parking spot, you poise your car at the end of a row, commanding 16 spaces. As soon as one of those 16 spaces opens up, you will get to park. How long do you expect to wait?

Pearls. I put 50 Black Seychelles (very valuable) pearls in a cigar box and 50 ordinary white pearls (not very valuable) in a second, identical cigar box. You get to choose a box and draw out a pearl. Then I will give you the rest of the pearls of the type you chose. It should be clear that your chances of getting the Black Seychelles are 50%. Suppose I allow you to mix the pearls in the two boxes in any way you choose. Can you improve your odds of getting the coveted Black Seychelles?

Percolation. Percolation theory is a relatively new branch of mathematics that deals with how one substance moves through another. The classic example is boiling water percolating through coffee grounds. We will introduce the subject by analyzing some games.

Hex. The game of HEX is played by two persons on the 9 by 9 array of hexagons on the next page. The players select sides on the board (up-down or left-right) and different colored playing pieces. They alternate turns by placing one of their pieces on any unoccupied hexagon. The object of the game is for one of the players (the winner) to complete an unbroken chain of pieces between his two sides. The chain may twist and turn freely but must be unbroken. The corners belong to both sides.

1. Must someone win the game?

2. Can both players win?

3. Can the player who goes first always win? If so, describe a winning strategy.

Now try a different game on the HEX board. The first player puts a piece on the center hexagon. The second player may place two markers anywhere she likes. The first player then gets to place one marker, the second player two, and so on. The object of the game is for the first player to complete an unbroken chain to a hexagon on the boundary. The second player's job is to prevent this.

4. Can either player always win? If so, describe a winning strategy.

5. What PSSSP techniques did you use to analyze these games?

For a final variation, try playing the game of HEX on an 8 by 8 checkerboard. Answer the questions 1-3 above for this square version.

HEX Board

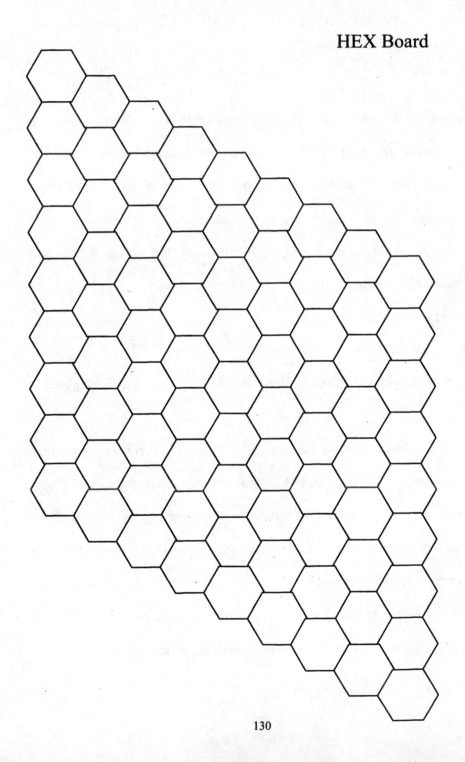

Pick's Theorem. A lattice polygon is a region made by connecting dots in a lattice, or square array. Below are ten examples of lattice polygons. Pick's Theorem tells how to determine the area of a lattice polygon with a formula that uses only the number of boundary dots and the number of interior dots. In the first example below, there are 11 boundary dots and 6 interior dots. Say the (horizontal) distance between two dots is 1.

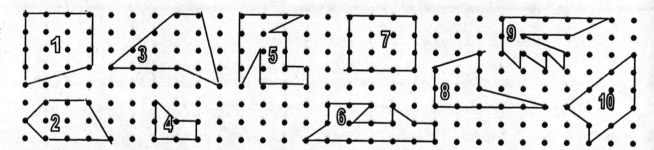

1. Determine the area of the ten sample lattice polygons. It helps to recall that the area of a triangle is one-half the base times the height.

2. Make up four more lattice polygons of your own and determine their areas. In each case note the number of boundary dots and the number of interior dots.

3. Find a formula (Pick's Theorem) that tells you how to get the area of a lattice polygon from the number of boundary dots and the number of interior dots. Check your answer on two additional lattice polygons.

Polyominoes. A domino is a 2 by 1 rectangle (we'll ignore the dots). We can think of a domino as two squares pasted together along a common edge. A tromino is then three squares pasted together along common edges. There are only two trominoes (draw them). If you think you can draw more than two, check that one of your trominoes can be obtained from another by flipping or rotating.

1. How many tetrominoes (4 squares) are there? Draw them.

2. How many pentominoes are there? Draw them.

The two types of trominoes can form a common region, for example a 2 by 3 rectangle:

3. For which two types of tetrominoes can a common region be formed? For example, 1 by 4 tetrominoes can form a 2 by 4 rectangle and so can 2 by 2 tetrominoes. Confirm your answers with drawings.

Planetary Voyage. (From Martin Gardner) I will assume you have on hand a dime and eight pennies. Instead of coins you can use buttons, checkers, or anything else that will serve as counters. I will now assume the role of magician.

Select any one of the planets in the 3 by 3 array below and put the dime on it. You are free to choose any of the nine planets and I have no way of knowing the choice you made. You will now move the dime a certain number of "hops" according to my direction. A hop is a move to the next planet above or below the one you are on, or to the left or right of the one you are on. No diagonal hops are allowed. On your first move you are to hop once for each letter in the name of the planet where you chose to put your dime. For example, if you start on Mars, hop once for each of the letters M-A-R-S. When you finish your move, put a penny on Venus, signifying its destruction with a Problemian death ray.

As an all-powerful magician, I am aware that you didn't land on Venus after your first move, and are thus able to make a second move, which is to make seven hops. Then put a penny on (blow up) Mars. After you have blown up Venus, Mars, or any of the succeeding planets, you are not allowed to hop onto them. This means you will have fewer and fewer places to hop as the game progresses.

- Move the dime seven hops, then put a penny on Mercury.

- Move the dime seven hops, then put a penny on Uranus.

- Move the dime seven hops, then put a penny on Neptune.

- Move the dime seven hops, then put a penny on Saturn.

- Move the dime seven hops, then put a penny on Jupiter.

- Move the dime seven hops, then put a penny on the Moon.

If you followed instructions correctly, you should now be on Pluto.

Mercury	Mars	Neptune
Uranus	Jupiter	Moon
Venus	Saturn	Pluto

The basic problem here is to explain how the trick works.

Try the procedure with seven hops replaced by spelling the word S-E-V-E-N. Does the trick still work? Try to blow up the planets in a different order.

Write a paragraph discussing which strategies gave you the most insight into the game.

Write a letter to your parents explaining how the game works.

Sessa's Wheat. The game of chess was invented by a mathematician named Sessa in the 15th century. The story goes that the King of Persia was so delighted by the game that he offered to let Sessa name his own reward. Sessa replied that he would take one grain of wheat for the first square on his 8 by 8 chessboard, two grains for the second square, four grains for the third square and so on, doubling the number of grains each time until the 64th square was reached. The king immediately called for a bag of grain to fill this simple request, but the reward turned out to be slightly more than he anticipated. Calculate how much wheat the King had to give to Sessa.

Seven Elevators. At a party, the superintendent of an apartment building tells you that his building has seven elevators. Each elevator stops on at most 6 floors. He also tells you that you can get to any one floor from any other floor without changing elevators (if you take the right elevator). What is the largest number of floors that the building could have?

Shoreline. What is the length of the shoreline of Mirror Lake (or some other lake at your university or in your town)?

Should You Switch? You are a contestant on a game show where one million dollars is hidden behind one of three closed doors. There is nothing behind either of the other two doors. You guess door 1, but before opening that door the game show host opens door 2 and shows you that nothing was hidden there. He offers you the chance to switch your guess to door 3. Should you switch?

Six digits. A six-digit number is a perfect square with all nonzero digits. The product of its digits is both a square AND a multiple of 7. What is the smallest such number?

Square roots. Find positive integers a,b,c so that $\sqrt{2+\sqrt{3}} = \dfrac{\sqrt{a}+\sqrt{b}}{c}$.

Stacking Rulers. You have an unlimited supply of one-foot rulers and a flat table, set on one end of the basketball court at Gampel Pavilion. You may stack the rulers in any way you wish on top of the table. How far can you extend your stack of rulers from the edge of the table? That is, how much of an overhang can you obtain? Does your answer change if you are only allowed to stack one ruler at each level?

Symmetry. People throughout history have been fascinated with symmetry. The idea is used in designing and decorating pottery, clothing and buildings.

A *symmetry* is a rigid motion (sliding, flipping, rotating) of a figure so that in its new position it looks exactly the same as in the original. Find all the symmetries of an equilateral triangle.

A *strip pattern* is a linear pattern that repeats infinitely often in both directions. For example, *abcabcabc...*, or *abacabac....*

See below for examples of strip patterns.

1. Have each person in your group construct a strip pattern. Then compare them in the group. What symmetries do they allow?

2. As a group, construct as many strip patterns as you can. Two strip patterns are different if they have different symmetry combinations. Describe the symmetries of each pattern.

3. Make up a classification scheme for strip patterns using symmetries. Use your scheme to classify each of the patterns below.

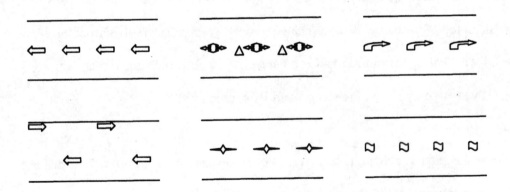

Three Ages. The hostess, at her 20th wedding anniversary party, tells you that the youngest of her three children likes to pose this problem, and proceeds to explain: "I normally ask guests to determine the ages of my three children, given the sum and product of their ages. Since Smith missed the problem tonight and Jones missed it at the party two years ago, I'll let you off the hook."

Your response is, "no need to tell me more, their ages are ..."

Three Bean Heaps. Starting with three heaps of beans containing 1, 4, and 4 beans, two players alternate moves until a player wins by removing the last bean. A move consists of

(i)   removing a heap that contains a single bean; or

(ii)   dividing a heap with two or more beans into two smaller heaps.

What is a winning strategy?

Three Squares. Using only elementary geometry (no trigonometry needed), show that angle C equals the sum of angles A and B.

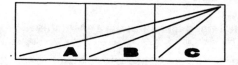

Trouble With Tribbles (From Dave Molnar) The following transmission arrived this morning from the U.S.S. Enterprise NCC-1701

Math... 102... problem-solving students...

forgive... primitive... paper... transmission...

computers... off-line... filled with... tribbles...

only... one hour... before... Enterprise... completely full...

Spock... no help... allergic...

Scotty... rigged up... space-time field displacement array...

don't know... how far back... to set it...

attaching... technical... memorandum...

help...

Kirk... out...

Technical Memorandum #Q17H0000-1: Tribbles

I have done some research into the unusual reproduction patterns of the Tribbles. Due to my heightened sensitivity, I fear that I shall be incapacitated before Lt. Scott has the time to re-configure the space-time field displacement array. I hope that these observations will provide the sufficient information for its calibration.

As we originally had only one tribble on the ship, we can logically conclude that they reproduce asexually. Our first tribble became mature after one hour, and has spawned a new tribble every hour since then. I have determined that all tribbles share this characteristic. The numbers of tribbles present each hour form a sequence with which I am familiar, but already my mental state is diminished to the point that I cannot recall the Earth terminology.

Can you help Kirk determine how far back to set the uh .. "space-time field displacement array" so that he will be rid of his trouble with tribbles?

True and False. (Sachar [26]) Assign a True or False to the statements in the following groups.

1. Statement 5 is false.

2. Statement 1 is false.

3. Statement 4 is true.

4. Only one of these is false.

5. Statements 2 and 3 have the same answer.

1. Statement 3 is true.

2. Statement 3 is false.

3. Statement 5 is false.

4. Statement 5 is true.

5. This and statement 3 have the same answer.

1. Statements 3 and 4 have the same answer.

2. At least four of these are false.

3. Statement 5 is true.

4. Statements 3 and 5 have different answers.

5. Statement 3 is true.

6. This and statement 1 have the same answer.

1. This and statement 5 have different answers.

2. Statement 10 is false.

3. This statement is true.

4. Statement 7 is true.

5. At least two of the above are false.

6. This and statement 9 have different answers.

7. Statement 6 is false.

8. Statement 2 is true.

9. Statements 3 and 4 have different answers.

10. Statement 3 is true.

Two Bean Heaps. There are two heaps of 10 beans each on the table. You and a partner alternate moves until all the beans are gone. The player to take the last bean(s) wins. A move consists of removing one bean from one of the piles, or of removing a bean from each pile. What is a winning strategy?

Weights. You have six weights. One pair is red, one pair white, one pair blue. In each pair one weight is a trifle heavier than the other but otherwise appears to be exactly like its mate. The three heavier weights (one of each color) all weigh the same. This is also true of the three lighter weights. In two separate weighings on a balance scale, how can you identify which is the heavier weight of each pair?

1. You have twelve weights, eleven of which are exactly the same, and a twelfth which is either lighter or heavier than the others, but otherwise looks similar. In three weighings on a balance scale, how would you determine which is the different weight and whether it is lighter or heavier?

2. You have 26 weights, one of which is slightly lighter than the other 25. How would you determine the light weight in three separate weighings on a balance scale?

Winning the Lottery. Why is winning the lottery a problem? How could you apply PProblem SSSolving to this problem?

Bibliography

1. Adams, J. L.,*Conceptual Blockbusting - A Guide to Betters Ideas*, 3rd Edition, Addison - Wesley Publishing Company, New York, Reading, MA, (1986).

2. _____, *The Care and Feeding of Ideas*, Addison - Wesley Publishing Company, New York, Reading, MA (1986)

3. Ayan, G. *Aha!*, Three Rivers Press, New York, (1997).

4. Bello, I. and Boitton, J. R., *Topics in Contemporary Mathematics*, 6th Edition, Houghton Miffin Company, Boston, New York, (1997).

5. Bennett, Briggs, and Morrow, *Quantitative Reasoning*, Addison- Wesley Publishing Company, Reading, MA, New York, (1996).

6. Beutelspacher, A., *Cryptology*, Mathematical Association of America, Washington, DC, (1994).

7. Brown, S. I., and Walter, M. I., *The Art of Problem Posing*, 2nd Edition, Lawrence Erlbaum Associates, Publishers, Hilldales, New Jersey, (1990).

8. Covey, S. *The Seven Habits of Highly Successful People*, Simon & Schuster, 1990.

9. DeFranco, T. C. and Hilton, P. (1999). Distinguishing Features of Mechanical and Human Problem-Solving. *Journal of Mathematical Behavior*, 18 (1), 79-84.

10. DeFranco, T. C. & Curcio, F., (1997). A Division Problem With a Remainder Embedded Across Two Contexts: Children's Solutions in Restrictive vs. Real-world Settings. *Focus on Learning Problems in Mathematics,* 19(2), 58-72.

11. DeFranco, T. C., (1996). A Perspective on Mathematical Problem Solving Based on the Performances of Ph.D. Mathematicians. *Research in Collegiate Mathematics Education.II* In Kaput, J., A. Schoenfeld, E. Dubinsky (Eds.), Issues in Mathematics Education Vol. 6, Conference Board of the Mathematical Sciences, American Mathematical Society & Mathematical Association of America, 195-213.

12. Gawain, S., *Creative Visualization*, Bantam Books, New York, (1982).

13. Halmos, P. R., *The heart of mathematics*, The American Mathematical Monthly 87(7) (1980), 519-524.

14. Hayes, J. R., *The Complete Problem Solver*, 2nd Edition, Lawrence Erlbaum Associates, Hillsdale, New Jersey, (1989).

15. Kadesch, R. R., *Problem Solving Across the Disciplines*, Prentice Hall, Upper Saddle River, (1997).

16. Konhauser, J. D. E., Velleman, D., and Wagon, S., *Which Way Did the Bicycle Go?*, The Mathematical Association of America, USA, (1996).

17. Krantz, S. G., *Techniques of Problem Solving*. The American Mathematical Society, Providence, RI., 1997.

18. Levine, M., *Effective Problem Solving*, 2nd Edition, Prentice Hall, Englewood Cliffs, New Jersey, (1994).

19. Ostrandeo, S., Schroedeo, L., and Ostrandeo, N., *Super - Learning 2000*, Delacook Press, New York, (1994).

20. Mason, J., Burton, L., and Stacey, K., *Thinking Mathematically*, Addison-Wesley. New York, (1985).

21. Platt, J. R., *The Art of Creative Thinking*, The Excitement of Science, Houghton-Mifflin, Boston, 1962.

22. Polya, G., *Mathematical Discovery*, (2 Vols.), John Wiley & Sons, New York, 1962, 1965.

23. Polya, G., and Kilpatrick, J., *The Stanford Mathematics Problem Book*, Teachers College Press, New York, 1974.

24. Polya, G., *How to Solve It: A New Aspect of Mathematical Method,* 2nd Edition, Princeton University Press, Princeton, New Jersey, (1988).

25. Roberts, A. W. and Varberg, D. E., *Faces of Mathematics*, 2nd Edition, Harper Collins Publishers, New York, NY, (1982).

26. Sachar, L., *Sideways Arithmetic from Wayside School*, Scholastic Inc. New York, NY, (1989).

27. Schoenfeld, A. H., *Mathematical Problem Solving*, Academic Press, Inc., 1985.

28. Schoenfeld, A. H., *Problem Solving in Context(s)*, The Teaching and Assessing of Mathematical Problem Solving (R.I. Charles and E.A. Silver, Eds.), vol. 3, The National Council of Teachers of Mathematics, Reston, VA, 1989, pp. 82-92.

29. Schoenfeld, A. H., *Learning to think mathematically: Problem solving, metacognition, and sense making in mathematics*, Handbook of Research on Mathematics Teaching and Learning (D.A. Grouws, ed.), Macmillan Publishing Co., 1992, pp. 334-370.

30. Silver, E. A., (Ed.), Teaching and learning mathematical problem solving: Multiple research perspectives, Lawtence Erlbaum Associates, Hillsdale, NJ, 1985.

31. Stanic, G. and Kilpatrick, J. *Historical Perspectives on Problem Solving in the Mathematics Curriculum*, The Teaching and Assessing of Mathematical Problem Solving (R.I. Charles and E.A. Silver, Eds.), vol. 3, The National Council of Teachers of Mathematics, Reston, VA, 1989, pp. 1-22.

32. Stevenson, F. W., *Exploratory Problems in Mathematics*, The National Council of Teachers of Mathematics, Inc., Reston, Virginia, (1992).

33. Steen, L. A., *On the Shoulders of Giants*, National Academy Press, Washington D.C., (1990).

34. Stinnett, N., and DeFrain, J., *Secrets of Strong Families*, Berkley Books, New York, 1985.

35. Tannenbaum, P. and Arnold, R., *Excursions In Modern Mathematics*, 2nd Edition, Prentice Hall, Englewood Cliffs, New Jersey, (1995).

36. Taylor, A. D., *Mathematics and Politics*, Springer - Verlag, New York, (1995).

37. Whimbey, A. and Lochhead, J., *Problem Solving and Comprehension: A Short Course in Analytical Reasoning*, Second Edition, Philadelphia, PA, The Franklin Institute Press, 1980.

38. Wickelgren, W., *How to Solve Problems*, Freeman, San Francisco, CA, 1974.

Some Useful Problem Solving Web Sites:

www.thinksmart.com

www.cut-the-knot.com

www.odyssey.org

www.exeter.edu/~rparris/default.html

www.dartmouth.edu/~chance/course/course.html

www.fas.harvard.edu/~grobis/fermiprb.html

www.hawaii.edu/suremath/journal.html

www.mathwright.com/

Appendix

Music to Solve Problems By

J.S. Bach – Air for the G String; Largos from Harpsichord Concertos in F Minor (BWV 1056) and C Major (BWV 975).

Beethoven – Concerto for Violin and Orchestra in D major, Op. 61.

Brahms – Concerto for Violin and Orchestra No. 1 in G Minor, Op. 26.

Chopin – Waltzes

Haydn – Symphonies No. 67 in F major and No. 68 in C Major.

Mozart – Concertos for Violin and Orchestra; Concertos for Piano and Orchestra; Eine Kleine Nachtmusik; String Quartets; Symphonies Nos. 29,32,39,40.

Pachelbel – Canon in D

Tchaikovsky – Concerto No. 1 for Piano and Orchestra in B Flat Minor, Op. 23; Violin Concerto in D Major, Op. 35

Telemann – Largo from Double Fantasia in G Major for Harpsichord

Vivaldi – The Four Seasons; Concerto in D Major for Guitar and Strings; Concerto in C Major for Mandolin, Strings, and Harpsichord

Some Modern Selections

William Duncan – Exultate – Music to Expand Learning

Andre' Gagnon – Lullaby for My Mother (from album *The St. Lawrence*)